THE WASTE BETWEEN OUR EARS

Protecting Our Environment and Improving Our
Soils with Source Separation

The Waste Between Our Ears:
How We Can Use Landfills to Regenerate Soils
and Disrupt Climate Change

Source Separation:
From Waste to Soil

The Carbon Recycle:
Utilizing Source Separation to Protect Our
Environment and Improve Our Soils

GERRY GILLESPIE

Acres U.S.A
Greeley, Colorado

Thanks and Acknowledgements

This book attempt to raise awareness of the urgent need for action on the many fronts of waste facing the world and in so doing, I acknowledge the many others who are attempting to do likewise. I recognise that many of the breakthroughs that we have in life are due to those who obstruct us as much as any who help, and for that they require the same acknowledgement as those who have brought to the conversation their kindness and support. In many instances, blockages force onto the determined a more refined thought process and delivery system.

Obstruction in many instances reflects a fear of change. In others it is due to greed inherent in patent and monetary systems which purport to encourage development while engendering wealth. In reality all they do is refine selfishness and greed for the benefit of a few and force the socially and intellectually hamstrung to pay for their very existence with their cash, their lives and their children's future.

In recognising those who assisted with the production of this book, I would like to name the more immediate few who have contributed directly and indirectly to its structure. My thanks to those who worked hard to attempt to correct my words and steer a more refined course. In all instances their efforts are acknowledged and respected.

Thanks to Carolyn Brooks, Mal Williams, Julie Schneller, Annemarie Meike, Richard Tong, Noel Pratt, Max Purnell, Russ Owens, Joanne Falvey and Editor Paul Meyer.

Thanks also to Acres U.S.A. for years of inspiration and ongoing support.

Table of Contents

FOREWORD:
On Changing Minds

This book is about the ability to think differently about discarded materials—about how to focus on their economic value rather than on how they are simply waste. To do this, you will need to be able to put your mind in a different place.

The late professor Robin Murray had developed great skill in the art of thinking differently.[1] He was a remarkable economist, recycler, author, and innovator. One of his great and ongoing contributions to the Zero Waste conversation, a movement that in many ways he led, was to add value to the economics of recycling in a world of differences. He once told me that his coming to an understanding of the value of wasted materials to the human economy was akin to realizing Nirvana.

In Robin's later years he encouraged those attending meetings to indulge in a small piece of poetry prior to the discussions, to refresh the mind and redirect the thinking. I hope that the structure of this book and its attendant poetry will help you approach the subject matter with a respect for Robin's copious skills and with an open heart for your own possibilities as a global citizen and an agent for change.

Gerry Gillespie
Australia, 2019

---

1. Robin Murray, *Zero Waste* (Washington, D.C.: Greenpeace Publications, 2002); Robin Murray, Creating Wealth from Waste (London: Demos, 1999).

Preamble

This book was written to enable all of us to understand the need to change our attitudes toward waste and to encourage people who are involved in or entering the "disposal" industry, which ostensibly cares for all community waste, to see that there is much more value in discarded materials than we currently think there is.

The modern disposal industry is still grappling to define what it should be doing, apart from making money for its shareholders. As demand is rising for more and improved recycling, the industry has slowly changed. But government regulation is slow to reflect that change and to create the necessary level playing field for all operators.

The waste industry grew as villages and cities combined into larger population centers. In centuries past, organic waste, the largest single component of material streams, readily found its way back to the soil.[2] As townships grew and farms began to increasingly rely on agricultural chemicals, however, this system faltered.

The increased and frenetic use of chemistry in growing food and the concurrent degradation of soils has led many people to rediscover the importance of composted organic materials and other biological products, which serve as a link between the community and the soil. Every single thing we are as humans depends on the things we eat. We all have an intense personal interest in healthy soil.

The disposal industry will be key to translating how organic material is used to reconnect its clients—all humanity—back to our mother, the soil. The social equity and political impact of recycling organic material is enormous!

---

2. "History of Waste Management and the Social and Cultural Representations of Waste," by S. Barles, *Encyclopedia of Life Support Systems*, https://www.eolss.net/Sample-Chapters/C09/E6-156-16-00.pdf/.

Humanity is facing climatic and agricultural crises that can only be solved by reconnecting to the soil.

Source-separating all organic material exponentially increases the value of every single thing collected, handled, processed, and sold. Importantly, the source separation of materials without crushing, contamination, or damage has been progressively demonstrated around the world as the most effective and valuable means of returning any-thing to its former or higher value. Through the efforts of the people of Germany, Wales, and members of the zero-waste communities around the world, we can now demonstrate how the economic advantages of source separation stack up. The removal of toxic and hazardous materi-als is essential to this process.

An understanding of this issue is key to a new future for the disposal industry and its fundamental role in local populations. It is no longer acceptable for the industry to simply view discards as a profit mechanism for disconnected, distant shareholders.

The best place for any organic material no longer in use is back in the soil. The best place to obtain value and benefit from other materials is in the local community.

Science and the Arts

The balance of this earth sublime
As nature has intended
Lives constantly within the stress
Humanity invented

The challenge of the times is this
If we can only face it
If science be what we design
The art is not to waste it

Introduction

Our "developed" world's consumption economy clearly needs rethinking. The current model is broken. It demands continual growth, but it does so with little thought of the environmental harm caused by today's economic thinking. Microscopic pollutants are pumped into the air, water, and land as if there were no future consequences. Man-made chemicals are applied to food and soils with little regard to the cumulative effects to human health and the obvious degradation caused to farmland. We have allowed the making of profits by a select few to denigrate all aspects of the built and natural environments. We make excuses to ourselves regarding the detritus being pumped out of the back end of this seemingly endless economic model.

It is our waste outputs that have caused climate change and destroyed our soils. Yet this very same detritus, if treated as a viable input into a next stage of our development, could readily become the point of salvation for all aspects of the human economy—if we could only change direction. That directional change will give us alternatives to what we are currently doing. In the short term, a change in thinking may at least buy us time to rethink our currently calamitous journey.

The resource recovery industry is a missing link in our thinking on these issues. It is a terrible tale of wasted words, of lost treasure, and of a febrile, angst-ridden, and potentially wasted future. Around 90 percent of our energy outputs and productive efforts are currently lost to the air and water, or directed to destruction or burial, in a mere matter of months after manufacturing. The obscenity of compulsive expenditure for economic theory has replaced care and community. In the developed world we are engrossed in an economic model in which we buy new items because we want them simply for the very sake of buying. This chain of manufacturing, consumption, and destruction is a process that begins with our disconnection and dislocation from planet earth and its soil—where we potentially lose both past and future by thinking that consumption is a replacement for economic development and that want is a replacement for need.

Before we go further, a caution. This book is not a history; that would imply that we have the past and future linked and referenced in one great story of consumptive greed. What we do have is part of a story that is only as old as the laughably misnamed "disposable container" made from recyclable material—verbal fallacy and oxymoron that flies in the face of thermodynamics. We can now clearly see where we are headed and should have noticed the dire need for change. We have among us many heroes of change, communities of care, and nations demonstrating that alternatives are genuinely possible on any scale. The zero-waste network, especially in Europe,[3] has demonstrated that there is another way to operate on the planet while still creating employment and making a profit. Many people, however, have not yet realized these benefits of change. They lack the key with which to open the door to meaningful recognition at a community level.

Our current consumption includes all elements of organic and inorganic materials. The organic model includes the loss of around 40 percent of agricultural food production at farm, at store, and at home. The potential to recover this loss provides an opportunity for a link back to the soil. This abuse of the food cycle highlights the destruction of ancient agricultural systems and soils through the misguided and misinterpreted application of the work of Justus von Liebig and others.[4] It exposes the financial desire of the chemical fertilizer industry to find excusable, justifiable, alternate uses for excess chemicals at the end of our two world wars. The second of these ushered in the abandonment of care and caution in favor of consumption and causality. It begat the period in which we truly began to eat away at the very soil beneath our feet on a grand scale. The same compulsive drive for

3. Zero Waste Europe website, accessed 5 July, 2019, https://zerowasteeurope.eu/.
4. "Justus von Liebig," Famous Scientists website, accessed 5 July, 2019, https://www.famousscientists.org/justus-von-liebig/.

increased profits, combined with munitions manufacturing, produced an urgent need to wage war—against both ourselves and our planet—in order to continue to build the greed economy.

On top of these lies we then had the Green Revolution,[5] which further increased the use of fertilizers, pesticides, and herbicides. To be more truthful, the Green Revolution *had us*—it gave us soil degradation practices that continue today.

The biological diversity in our soils and the very plants that cause rain cry out for rest and recovery. Instead, we poison them with the insane outputs of biologically ignorant pharmacological drug peddlers whose notion of control is herbicide applied with pesticide to genetically modified plants. Biased and unproven science is locked in the closed mind of secret intellectual property with the wanton mantras of profits before procreation and careers before civilization. The ad hoc application of chemistry under the "more-on" principle continues to destroy soils and their biological structures at rates that are now declared by the UN to be only sufficient for around sixty more yearly harvests using the chemically driven industrial agriculture model. All of this is wrapped up in the false, concocted story that we need to increase food production to feed the rising masses of humanity.

This is simply not true—there is more than enough food in the world for the current population. People are starving because of the politics of greed, wars for profit, modern agricultural practices, the destruction of soils, and ineffective and inefficient transport—not because of a lack of food.

The solutions to the desecration of our soils can begin with stopping what we are doing. We need to change management practices and engage the community in a political and social conversation about food production. This can include giving back into the soil the same organic materials we took from them in the first place, enabling them to rebuild the complexity they require to function biologically.

---

5. "Harmful Effects of the Green Revolution," Kevin Lee, Sciencing website, updated 23 April, 2018, https://sciencing.com/harmful-effects-green-revolution-8587115.html/.

There are many, many regenerative, holistic, and subsistence farmers who, if given half a chance, could readily show us the way home to the soil—if we would only stop to listen to their simple story. However, for us to listen—not as an alternate few but as a broader community—we must have a point of total engagement in the issue of soil and food. I believe that we can use the organic outputs of our homes, businesses and farms as this engagement point. People do indeed understand the essence of this matter because it is as firmly linked to the expression of their genes, through their children, as it is to the air they breathe.

Our organic waste, which comprises more than 50 percent of the total waste material we produce, is a starting point for our conversation on future food production systems.

If we remove organic material from our waste streams, we have a mix of mainly inert material mixed with a small percentage of toxics, which should not be there in the first place.

Using the Right Language

I will expound upon these matters in some detail as we progress, but for now there is a need to establish the base proposition upon which the "waste" calamity that now befalls us began. More than any other issue, the story regarding "waste" is about language—what and how we name things and how those names, once given, become omnipotent and intractable. Not unlike obsessive beliefs, once given the name "waste," a material has to be redeemed in the eyes of the recycling faithful before it can once again regain any value in the full light and sight of the human economy. How do we manage to change the structure and name of a full—as opposed to an empty—glass bottle? One is called "Coke" and the other is called "waste," yet the quality of the bottle changes not one iota—only our consideration of it and our desire to treat it with respect does.

Even the recycling fraternity have been conned into thinking that these things are somehow different. We agree that our bottle has lost its sugar content and therefore its desirability. It has also lost its cushion for careful transport, its sweet liquidity, and its satin-brown color—but it is no different in terms of external packaging material. Somehow, however, it must find its own way home to be smashed out of shape and remade in the eyes of humanity. Was the joy of value only for its contents, a one-way trip to be appended to the fat-enhanced torso of a future diabetic? As liquid lost to liver harm and doomed to discharge, but now empty—the servant of the manufacturer, the carriage of convenience, the container of contentment, now vanished and vanquished from the world of industry? It is only a sad and empty bottle, maybe recycled under duress or redeemed in some artificial container deposit scheme in which the small change, earlier added to the sale price, is now returned to the redeemer of this victim of degradation. Surely if we respected the bottle, the earth from which it was made, the environment into which its excess heat and gases from the manufacturing process were dumped, then a return process for such packaging material would be inbuilt as a matter of course into the product. The process of manufacturing, the transportation of goods, the sale, and the disposal process are all predicated on a lack of awareness for the earth on which we stand and the soil from which we live.

The process of recycling materials is seen as a battle against waste and, in some minds, as an added cost to the community. This can only be the case, however, if the process of recovery is seen as an addition to the comfort system of engineered waste management. How long will it be before we begin to actually think of truly closed materials cycles? Some local government authorities complain at the extra costs they must endure to recycle materials, when surely most are aware that local authorities have no money. Like all other forms of government, they use your money to subsidize disposal on your behalf and at your expense—most of the time to landfill or, heaven forbid, to incineration. Both landfill and incineration externalize vast costs in terms of air, water, and ground pollution to the environment. As a senior waste and landfill manager in New Zealand once told me, "all landfills leak, and water runs downhill."

Some engineers will tell you that that organic waste should go into landfill because, with a gas capture system, they can get enormous amounts of methane, which they then use to generate energy. In some instances, even they believe this. Now keep in mind that methane (leave out all the other gases) on its own is about thirty times more harmful as a greenhouse gas than CO_2.[6] The most courageous of landfill managers will tell you that their gas efficiency capture rate is about 90 percent of output. This is doubtful but assume for the moment that it is possible. It means that for every 90 tons of methane captured, 10 tons is lost to the atmosphere. Another way to look at this is that for every 90 tons of methane captured, 300 tons of CO_2-equivalent is pumped intentionally into the atmosphere. And companies get environmental credits for creating this environmental degradation! It is insane that "environmental credits" encourage such behavior.

Apart from landfill, the other extremely dangerous example of waste management is incineration. Keep in mind that only materials that are organic in origin will burn in an incinerator—the rest is turned into a very toxic mixed ash, which creates a range of serious problems. So, for something to burn, it had to originally came from a plant. Even plastics made from fossil fuels, scientists tell us, are organic in origin. But we know that all plastics are recyclable, even if we don't do it as yet. Plastics are slowly killing the planet by progressively strangling everything in the sea—but more on that later.

Up to 70 percent of everything in a waste stream, depending of course on the source, is organic: trees, grass, food, dead animals, manure, biosolids, paper, cardboard, etc. All of this material, through various processes that will be outlined later, can be returned to the earth as a range of valuable products to improve soil quality. Put simply, there is no need for incineration. The reason companies offer incineration services to governments, which then force this practice

---

6. "Why There's More Greenhouse Gas in the Atmosphere than You May Have Realized," by Zoe Loh, et al., Commonwealth Scientific and Industrial Research Organization of Australia, published 11 June, 2019, https://blog.csiro.au/more-greenhouse-gas-in-atmo-sphere-than-you-may-have-realised/.

on communities, is because it is worth a lot of money. Incinerators are extremely expensive to build and operate. From the financier's perspective, the best bit is that they operate for about twenty-five years and that the misguided, ill-informed ratepayer pays for the whole lot. The

Put simply, there is no need for incineration. The reason companies offer incineration services to governments, which then force this practice on communities, is because it is worth a lot of money.

waste companies love it because they charge us for mashed-up collections, then they charge us for transport, then they charge us to dump it, and then they make electricity out of the 70 percent that burns. Then they charge us—the very people who paid for the whole operation in the first place—a lot of money to buy back our own energy. What a financial model!

This might be laughable for its brashness if the incineration were the only consideration, but the practice has other very serious negative consequences. Burning waste creates toxic ash and noxious gases such as dioxin and furan that can cause cancer in humans and animals. No company has yet been able to comprehensively demonstrate that their chimney outputs are continually without pollutants. On top of this, if you look at the simplicity of recycling organics, it is much easier and more valuable to pay someone to source-separate the organic elements and recycle them than it is to pay a waste company to burn it and, in doing so, potentially harm your community.

Changing the Process

What we are talking about, of course, are better systems of management. Landfill and incineration grew out of ignorance, and we have placed additional layers on top of them to make them more expensive. This is all because bankers and waste managers can make a great deal of money by making the system much more complicated. So, as is the case with many of life's mysteries, simpler is not only better—it is a great deal cheaper. Recycling instead of utilizing a landfill or an incinerator provides local employment and many local business opportunities.

In reality, if a waste company is in charge, in many instances, they will use the same processes, functions, vehicles, and misnomers to make recycling difficult or at least very expensive. Be it the management of waste or the management of recycling, a complex industry has been built up around two material streams—recycled and not recycled—that have their own specific operating premises. In this industry, materials are collected and compacted (mashed) and mixed (comingled) together so as to make it as difficult as possible to separate the components of the mix, at the same time comprehensively devaluing anything collected and mashed together.

Of course, in such collection processes the objective is supposedly to recycle much of the material. This of itself creates a situation where the community, through its local governing authority, is paying exorbitant amounts of money to build expensive facilities to separate the very materials that would not have been mixed together in the first place had they been source-separated. The relative expense of comingled collections provides a twisted justification that supposedly demonstrates environmental care and concern, when in fact it simply justifies the continuance of waste production and support for the status quo. In fact, it is desirable in the eyes of some "economists" to produce waste to demonstrate how productive we are. Theoretically, in their eyes, the more waste we make, the more money we must be making—because more waste means we have made more sales.

Modern economic perversions have created a situation in which cheap and/or slave labor in remote countries can now create new goods for less than it costs to recover old materials for remanufacturing. None of the calculations provided to demonstrate that new materials are cheaper than recycled, though, ever include the costs of the environmental harm of production. It accumulates like a spreading pox in diverse regions of manufacturing countries. On a visit to Beijing in 1997, I was told that of the 700-plus river systems in the country at that time, less than 10 had potable water. Such horrific statistics lead to the many descriptions we hear and see of the number of planets we will need to colonize to continue this form of practice in the future.

These processes, of course, will ultimately lead to the collapse of our current economic model, if not the whole of humanity. Manufacturing production in all instances ultimately comes back to the soil. For a country to make goods for export, it requires inputs from agriculture both for the industry itself and to sustain the community that makes the goods. Without healthy soil we cannot have a viable economy, human or natural. US President Franklin D. Roosevelt was right—if you have no soil, you have no country. There is, of course, the increasingly dominant, supposedly 'safe' option of hydroponic vegetable production and of aquaculture. Both systems could be greatly improved with less chemistry, better logistics and data management. However, we are still fundamentally tied to the soil and the fundamental cycles that sustain it.

Changing Perception

If we are to truly eliminate waste in word and deed, then we need alternatives. If we are going to avert the destruction of humanity at the feet of mammon in the belief that consumption of both our soils and souls is necessary to make a commercial profit above all else, then we will need to get the words right and be aware of the alternatives to wasted production!

This story will hopefully provide a different perspective on the things we discard. It is my intention to get people thinking about the attributes and potential alternate uses of the materials we all throw away, the things in which our purchases came—packaged, wrapped, skinned, bottled, or stacked, from which the contents have been removed. That is to say, materials we have no immediate use for in their current form. This book will not—indeed cannot—be comprehensive; the uses of any one material are determined as much by human innovation and need as the perceived current use of the product.

The story of what is wasted, of course, is not the same in every country. Collection methods vary, depending on the perceived value of any product and its immediate local use. However, this, as we will see, can change, depending on that ultimate value. We all have much to learn from others in this regard. The application of any given product to a specific function or use can determine its inherent value, and this value may not be reflected in how you initially see the product.

As I hope to demonstrate in this story, not only have we had it totally wrong in regard to those things we call waste—we have missed some of the greatest values in terms of family, community, soil, and economy by mistreating materials we no longer have need of. We desperately need to change our perception of the concept of waste if we are to begin to respect the planet and all it does for us on a daily basis. As a human population, our attitudes to waste have not changed in recent times, even when the climate was telling us we were wrong and what we were doing was a path to certain destruction. We have not managed to change our concept of waste even when it was demonstrated that we were destroying our soils through our overuse of chemical fertilizers, our lack of engagement, and our misunderstanding of the importance of returning organic matter to the land. We have not managed to change our concept of waste even when it was demonstrated to us that it was economically far more beneficial for our local communities to use local materials to create local jobs by source-separating, collecting, reusing, and selling the things we no longer needed.

We have made our systems of management more complex, when all sensible research and outcomes have shown that what we need is simplicity and practicality. But the problem in this instance is that very large companies make enormous profits by making systems more complex. Big trucks loaded with convoluted hydraulics collect mixed materials and transport them to a big building with convoluted hydraulics, within which a complex belted recovery operation spins, whirrs, hums, blows, and vibrates while theoretically separating the materials into categories using a combination of human and mechanical means. It is very expensive, and of course every expense to the waste contractor carries with it a substantial profit margin.

Combine this with the notion that the "waste" and "recycling" sectors, in what we call "the industry" are now almost inseparable and that the private and public sectors are in the main all part of the one big family. Complicated and expensive management systems also run the contract that runs the management systems. This in turn justifies large expenses for taxpayers, with little return on their investment apart from a subsidized landfill or incinerator—both of which are a proven threat to human health. This notion makes the objective of attaining a dramatic reduction in waste all the more difficult and expensive.

I made the point at an Orbit Conference in Renne, France, in 2012—in juxtaposition to a claim from an earlier UN speaker that it

As I hope to demonstrate in this story, not only have we had it totally wrong in regard to those things we call waste—we have missed some of the greatest values in terms of family, community, soil, and economy by mistreating materials we no longer have need of.

was a basic human right for every home on the planet to have a waste bin—that in Australia in 1788, upon the arrival of the British convict fleet, the locals had a zero waste system in place. It was one that had been in place for tens of millennia, simply because the outputs of any one process were the inputs to another. The aboriginal population lived with, rather than in opposition to, nature. They understood that if you looked after the land it would look after you.

Recycling for the sake of community benefit requires an ability to see small things as part of a much bigger picture, or at least to perceive them as a material that may have many uses as part of a functional model. To do this you often need to change your perception of the material you are looking at. What are its properties? What is it made of? There is a need to ask what the best use might be for a product in terms of local benefit. Remote locations have often created the need for innovation to gain reuse benefit when transportation for reuse or recycling is not an option. In any case, local use is almost always better use.

Glass bottles for milk, up until around twenty years ago, could be used as many as eighty to one hundred times depending on the weight of the glass they were made from and how they were handled. As a result, they went back for refilling. This process was destroyed by disposable plastic bottles and plastic-lined cardboard containers. In remote areas in the early 1900s, in the event that people could not return the bottles for refilling, they would tie a length of paraffin-dipped string around the base of the bottle neck, light it, wait for the flame to die, and then dip the bottle immediately into cold water. The neck would break off, giving them a very functional and useful drinking glass after a light sanding.

As paper production increased and cardboard packaging became more universal, it made sense to reuse the fiber as much as possible. Paper has been recycled throughout history, originally in some instances having been made from recycled rags. When it came to be utilized in large quantities, wood became the primary source of fiber. Although we now have the means to transport paper and cardboard as reading material and packaging into remote rural areas, it is not always economically or environmentally sensible to return packaging to a larger city for recycling because the return journey is not included in the upfront cost of the product. However, paper is only wood fiber—if mixed with biosolids, manure or other organic waste it will make a wonderful compost for poor soils. Such products should find very ready local markets, given observation of appropriate regulations.

Of necessity, most of the on-the-ground examples I shall give in this book are from Australia—simply because I have worked in recycling there for over thirty years. To demonstrate that what I am proposing is achievable, I have also included details on an amazing Welsh government effort that has transformed its recycling program from last in recycling to close to the world leader in less than twenty years. I have also listed a few other exceptional experiences from around the world that I have obtained while travelling. My focus on Australia highlights the slow progress of recycling when it is tied to government in partnership with the waste industry. Australia is as good an example as you can get of vested interests blocking progress in both waste and recycling. Both recyclers and wasters are doing very well from the industry; in many ways they are stifling forward movement.

This then is our focus and should be the principal point of discussion. As singer-songwriter Charlie McGee says, "there is no such thing as waste"![7] With the vast majority of our discard streams being organic, a central focus of this conversation must be on soils and how we will feed ourselves if we continue to abuse them. There is an important connection for the human community back to the soils through organic waste. There will always be a number of things that may prove difficult in a given local situation, but, given thought and effort, difficulties and constraints can be overcome to provide local value—this has already happened in many parts of the world.

In efforts to change our local situation to one of complete materials use and of zero waste, we may find that local waste managers generally tend to have a base fascination and intimacy with mediocrity. They fear the word "zero" as if it were death. Total recycling, they think, may ruin their profession. The aim of this book is to highlight some of the examples and models that demonstrate that zero waste is not only desirable for your community—it is achievable.

The only place that waste exists is between our ears, because waste is not a fact—it is a concept.

---

7. "No Such Thing as Waste," *Formidable Vegetable*, by Charles McGee, http://formidablevegetable.com.au/.

Between Our Ears

The waste between our ears gives rise
To misplaced piles of money spent
On complex steel all shaped and bent
By engineers who waste your time
Concocting crass veracity
For bankers who will loan to you
The many millions which will be
A debt to all community
Complexified simplicity
Collective joint incumbency
The science of numerosity
Incinerating rates for free

All money spent assists the rich
Shareholder dividends and fee
To help your way toward an end
That neither do you want nor see

CHAPTER 1
Between Our Ears

The only place waste exists in any natural system is between human ears.

Waste is a concept. It is not a fact. Through misuse of language, it has colonized the human mind with a base deception. When we define things as waste, we make them fit into our predetermined "waste" categories. Once defined as waste, we give ourselves permission to treat items as such, and thus we allow and introduce the collection method, the partial processing, and the penultimate waste. If we don't define materials as waste, we are obliged to simply treat them as what they are—as materials.

Nature has no waste. The outputs of one thing become the inputs of another—nature simply treats things as they are and uses them for continual benefit in a circular system in which they are disposed from one circumstance to the next.

A community with a focus on zero waste has the opportunity to place itself back into the cycle of nature.

There is no such tangible thing as waste, in precisely the same way that there is no such tangible thing as a public holiday. When we nominate a day of the week as a public holiday, this does not change the form, the structure, the weather, or the time of that day—we simply change how we might behave or react during it. A good, bad, or indifferent public holiday is determined by our attitude toward it. The same is true of wasted materials.

If they were not defined as waste and were instead source-separated into categories that did not contaminate each other, a very large percentage of materials would follow the disposal processes of nature and would be available for their next functional use. If only we could provide the right tools, motivation, and information to source-separate our outputs into categories and to generate benefit for our communities. This is currently only happening in select communities where the focus is on reduced environmental impact, maximum community benefit, and local employment.

Wasted Incentives

I would suggest that this is because we don't recognize the actual value in products or materials. Our value propositions in regard to disused materials are artificial because we categorize them as wasted products, even when we do recover them. We train people in the management of waste, give them tools to manage waste, and then appoint them to manage waste. If we then use these very same people to manage our recycling programs, using the same collection containers, vehicles, and training, the most likely result is that we will get much more waste, because the responsible people are trained to manage waste, not to manage resource recovery businesses. In fact, it could readily be argued that if people in the public sectors of local or state management have never owned or operated a business; putting them in charge of the recovery of resources to be used as a business input is counter-intuitive. In the main, they have no concept of base value, secondary use, manufacturing process, or market value.

Why should we be surprised when we give waste managers big bulldozers and holes in the ground that we end up with filled-in holes? An even more terrible alternative is allowing them to borrow enormous amounts of public funds and to accrue long-term debt to build an incinerator. In that case, the result is toxic ash and carcinogens in the air. Professor Ian Boyd, Chief Scientific Advisor in the United

Kingdom's Department for Environment, Food, and Rural Affairs, said this of incineration:

> If there is one way of extinguishing the value of the materials fast, it's to stick it in an incinerator and burn it. Now it may give you energy at the end of the day, but actually some of those materials, even if they are plastics, with a little bit of ingenuity, can be given more positive value. And one of the things that worries me is that we are taking these materials, we're putting them in incinerators, we're losing them forever, and actually we're creating carbon dioxide out of them as well, which is not a great thing, when in fact we could be long-term storing them until we have the innovative technologies to re-use them and to turn them into something that is more positively valued. And this brings me to a more general point about landfill . . . landfill is actually a very low marginal-cost method for storing materials—highly resistant materials such as plastics and metals—for a long period of time. We shouldn't lose sight of the fact that in a few decades time, or maybe a bit longer, we might be mining our landfill sites for the resources they contain, and rather than put some of those resources into incinerators and just lose them forever we might want to think differently about the landfill sites.[8]

Professor Boyd's astute observation leads to the obvious conclusion that if you want to store material for later recovery, there is a need to eliminate all organic material from the mix. Therefore, a primary element in this process would be source separation to enable the removal of all organic waste, including paper and cardboard, to prevent methane generation.

We clearly need to give managers different tools, motivation, and information if we want a different result. If we keep providing the infrastructure for waste, training to manage waste, and financing for waste, there is a good chance we will continue to get waste. Material

---

8. "Chief Defra scientist says incineration extinguishes innovation," United Kingdom Without Incineration Network, published 1 February, 2018, http://ukwin.org.uk/2018/02/01/chief-defra-scientist-says-incineration-extinguishes-innovation/.

outputs from any individual, organization, or community need to be managed by social enterprise and business developers, not waste managers. We have created a circumstance where not only the waste companies, but the recyclers, too, see themselves as needing to have waste to provide themselves permanent employment. They would all potentially see the elimination of waste as a career threat. Waste companies are not interested in community outcomes—and quite rightfully, given their employed role: a primary interest for the general manager of a waste company is the dividend going back to the shareholders. That's their job description and how they advance in their careers. The more community money they can extract from government to do that job— to handle materials, to provide more trucks, and to increase expense to the customer—the better it is for their shareholders. Comingled recycling collections for the waste industry are a brilliant income generator—they are the next best thing to total mixed and mashed waste collections. In some ways they are better, because they need two sets of trucks, more elaborate equipment, and bigger buildings. In some instances, one company can have multiple contracts for collections, processing, and disposal.

The waste industry will always tell you that people will not recycle because they are lazy or ignorant. However, it is of course in the waste companies' best interest to tell you that. Keep in mind that in the past twenty years the country of Wales has gone from 5 percent recycling nationally to second best in the world—you can't do that if your community is lazy or ignorant. The fewer people engaged in the recycling process, the more mixed materials you have. In that case, the waste industry argues that we need more machinery and facilities if we want to recycle materials after they have all been mashed together. However, source separation is not only cheaper in the long run—it also eliminates the need for all those clunky, huge, expensive Materials Recovery Facilities (MRFs), which are built for the benefit of bigger contracts. Coincidentally, source separation means communities can make even more money from recycling. Simply replace the expensive trucks and MRF machinery with more jobs on the street and curbside sorting vehicles.

The Government of Wales completed an analysis in 2008[9] that clearly told them that the cheapest and most effective way to collect quality recyclables was for households to source-separate their own materials. Trained collectors then gently place these clean materials into designated compartments on side-loading curbside trucks. The best and cheapest outcome, according to this research, is direct sort to a vehicle. This has since been substantiated by additional research by Wales. The collection vehicle then takes the clean, sorted material for bulking up and delivery to market. It makes sense for no other reason than it delivers the highest quality product, with less waste to landfill; and this is as true for food waste as it is for an empty glass bottle. Any errors made by the householder are corrected by the collectors, who leave incorrect or contaminated materials in the collection crate for the householder to put in the residual bag or bin. This has resulted in less than 0.5 percent contamination by weight in places where this system has been well managed.

Current recycling programs that market to Asia are having materials rejected due to lack of source separation. The materials are, for all intents and purposes, mixed waste. Source separation is the answer to quality, quantity, and sale price. A great deal of the investment in these systems should go into engaging the community, developing local markets for quality product, and returning the profits from those markets to the local community. The absolute opposite is true of systems currently implemented by the waste industry. Their number one best option for profit is to collect mixed waste in a single bin and take it to an extraordinarily expensive, stainless-steel MRF, which sorts at great cost to the community that already paid for the expensive MRF. If a community uses the waste industry model, the industry controls the transport, the processing, and the disposal. All three are great profit centers because they are very expensive for the local community.

Waste industry contractors, following their business model, will maximize the cost of collections per home and then maximize the

9. "Waste Management in Wales: Municipal Recycling," Wales Audit Office, published 15 November, 2018, http://www.audit.wales/publication/waste-management-wales-municipal-recycling/.

cost of processing by building you a dirty Mixed Biological Treatment plant (MBT) or an MRF. Then they or another company will be involved in the cost of the disposal or sale of the outputs to either a landfill or an incineration facility, all the while making the process as complicated as possible and beating the community about the head with its own environmental regulations, with every bulldozer, every truck, every ton of cover, every incinerator scrubber, and every ton of toxic waste making them a profit. This profit is generally exported to the waste company's home boardroom or country of origin.

There is no such thing as government funds—there is only the individual householder's contribution to the public purse. Every bit of money passed on to a French, Australian, American, or Italian waste conglomerate is taken from the pocket of the average householder and is money lost to the local community. We, as the guardians of the public purse, deserve to have the money we spend on the "away" process regarded as an investment of public money, and like any other investment it should generate a return—for the community—not just for waste companies, be they foreign or local. An investment of a different kind for a different outcome will give the community more jobs, a better environment, better soils, and a safer future. A sensible investment in simplicity and recycling systems with the correct tools, motivation, and information will give everyone what the Welsh government discovered: more jobs, better products, local investment, and community benefit—all at less cost. Recycling clearly works!

Thinking Differently

To develop a different perspective on the materials we discard, we need to consider their physical attributes, the elements of their qualities, and their potential alternate uses. That is to say, materials that we have no immediate use for in their current form may be viable for another application or in another form. We know their fundamental structure, their chemical make-up, and their biological nature. This opens the door to many new functions. The development of alternate uses will never be comprehensive, in that the uses of any one material are determined as much by clever human innovation, discovery, and need as they are by the perceived current use of the product.

John D. Barrow, in his 2007 book, *New Theories of Everything*, says that "our present pace of discovery of truths about seemingly fundamental things does not necessarily indicate that we are about to converge upon the spot where all the treasure lies buried." However, we do have many of the necessary tools to prevent loss and waste—even if our concepts are currently limited.

The story of what is wasted, of course, is not the same in every country. Collection methods vary, depending on the perceived value of any product and its immediate local use. However, as we will see, this can change depending on the perception of that ultimate value. The application of any given product to a specific function or use can determine its inherent value, and this value may not be reflected in what we initially see the product as. I will demonstrate in this story of what we call waste that not only have we had it totally wrong, but that we desperately need to change our perception of the concept of waste if we are to begin to respect the planet and all that it does for each of us.

I have already mentioned speaking with zero waste author and economist Professor Robin Murray on this subject. As an economist, when he suddenly realized the value and community benefit inherent in what was referred to as "the waste stream," that it was like "walking into a valley of wealth—a great Nirvana." Our attitudes toward waste have not changed in recent times, even as the climate has been telling and showing us that we have been wrong. We have not managed to change our concept of waste even when it was demonstrated that we were destroying our soils through our overuse of chemicals, through our lack of engagement, and by our not understanding the true value of returning organic materials to the land to change agriculture. We have not managed to change our concept of waste even when it was demonstrated to us that it is economically more beneficial for local communities to use local materials to create local jobs and local value.

The Waste Industry

The issue of waste and its management over the past fifty years has become an increasingly stratified field, with qualified professionals in the fields of education, collection, mechanical engineering, materials recovery, incineration, and landfill. It has employment positions and indeed multiple interests in the private sector, local government, state regulation, and national environment, many of which share the same qualifications, reference points, ideology, machinery, truths, and myths. As such, it is a field of endeavor that enables a ready transfer of employment from the private to the public sector and back again, to enable career shift and personal and monetary improvement.

As pressure and competition from the community sector and the not-for-profit areas has increased over the years, the professional waste industry has been forced by public awareness to move more into re-cycling—a field in which, as an industry, it had little initial skill. This meant that waste industry employees were compelled to absorb many of the issues associated with recycling programs to maintain their commercially competitive edge. In places where small, regional local authorities, through the impetus of community groups, have introduced elements of a recycling program over the years, both commercial contractors and council staffs have been required to at least be aware of the public demands for recycling and to make some effort to display recycling intent.

One of the unfortunate aspects of constant staffing changes, as individuals move from the public to private sectors or from one district to another, is that recycling systems in local areas that were introduced thirty and forty years ago and had evolved, at least in part, into more comprehensive and successful programs, have often reverted to a primary "bottles and cans" stage. This is also due to tendering of community-developed enterprises out to the private sector, personal ownership issues, and individual skills or lack of them and the mutual need of the private contractors and local authorities to ensure change is by their mutual agreement rather than via revolution. This has meant that otherwise beneficial outcomes have become less attainable—especially if the person engaged to perform the task is protecting a personal position or career path as their primary interest.

There is always the risk that unless the industry makes some attempt to display its interests in recycling that communities might come to their senses and take over the materials collections, processing, and sales themselves and retain all the value locally. Current methods of collection and processing in most modern countries are very expensive for local communities, and a large percentage of local contracts are the contractor's built-in profit margins. This raises the issues associated with efficiency in terms of material collection. It also begs questions associated with the mystery of the waste industry—some local government bodies think there is some form of exotic process associated with waste and recycling collections, leading them to believe that this work needs to be done by someone other than locals. The local tragedy is that the waste industry sees it as far more efficient to collect all materials in a "mixed stream." As an alternative, the social enterprise, non-profit, or local private enterprise will prefer source separation because any clean, separated product has more reuse, resale, and recycling value. This creates a considerable conundrum for the waste industry, in that this same industry, which is the end point of increasingly destructive consumerism, is now also dabbling, under public pressure, with greater and varying degrees of success in the field of recycling—an enterprise that is arguably the antithesis of its primary function. I would think they would be the first to admit that in many instances they do not do this well.

Commercial waste operators, however, have not lost sight of the fact that the more they collect materials with single-driver-operated, side-loader vehicles, and the more materials are mixed together under compaction, the more expensive they are to separate back out into single streams in MRFs—which of course are an expense that is unnecessary in the first place if materials are collected separately. Collection fees are only one of the payments individual citizens make to waste management companies. Households also pay enormous amounts of money to separate the materials that are compacted together in a mechanical side-loader collection vehicle on the false premise of efficiency.

So basically, we as householders—who pay for the collection compaction vehicle, the staff, the transport costs, and the MRF—are often further penalized by the collected materials being processed somewhere else. This is also a cost in our rates, so we don't get the benefit of the jobs we are paying for, and in any case the materials are of poor quality and have a very low sale value. That value, such as it is, may not be returned to the local community, so we lose on that as well. The more external contractors are used to collect and process your wasted materials, the more expensive it is for the local community, both in terms of the lost assets and the lost employment.

If we truly are going to regard source-separated collected material as a community asset rather than as a waste, it is surely time we start to collect it as such, value-add to it, and use it to the best benefit of the local community. We also need the localized ability to reuse materials as close as possible to the community from which they were collected. Again, look to the Government of Wales, which, as I have already mentioned, is now rated as one of the top three recycling countries in the world.[10] It is expanding collection systems in which materials are source-separated at the home and then carefully loaded onto trucks at the curbside. As a result, aspects of the industry in Wales are facing major changes. It is always worthwhile to keep in mind that government contractors are driven by profits for shareholders; their main function is not quality outputs and increased employment but rather maximized mechanical handling, higher profits, and fewer jobs. If a community takes the sensible and community focused source-separation alternative, it will be in direct conflict with this commercial objective. If benefit for and of the local community is the focus, that community will obtain the maximum beneficial value from the product at the local level. Such an objective is totally contrary to the focus of the private waste sector.

This inevitably means that the principal driver for change in the waste industry must be the local community. It has been demonstrated in many places that better outcomes in the recycling sector lead to quality products and increases in local employment. When community

---

10. "Recycling – Who Really Leads the World?" by Joe Papineschi, Peter Jones, and Rob Gillies, Eunomia website, published 13 March, 2017, https://www.eunomia.co.uk/reports-tools/recycling-who-really-leads-the-world/.

organizations are involved, materials are often collected in different ways depending on location, end use, process, and application. Crucially, local use means maximizing value at the local level. This base conflict between waste industry financial objectives and community needs will ultimately mean total change: a 100 percent shift in the management of residual materials—not as waste but as community assets. Such an assertion will seem almost rhetorical to people involved in the community recycling movement today. However, thirty and forty years ago, as we contested this space with the waste industry monoliths, it was a very considerable battle, and the injuries—physical, personal, and financial—were many. Over the past forty-five years, the world has seen dramatic increases in recycling, to the point where there are now hundreds of communities worldwide that have a goal of zero waste.

The concept of zero waste—described in more detail in another chapter—while initially derided, has developed remarkable and credible results, not only in dramatically reduced waste to landfill and incineration but also in community employment, empowerment, resource use, and reduced environmental impact. It has swept the world with amazing speed and many achievements, simply because it makes sense. An increased awareness of the harm that humanity is visiting on its only planet is driving the protection of life's essentials of air, soil, and water. This forms the basis for the zero-waste movement, which focuses on the effective and efficient use of all recovered resources.

Of these resources, which are the total mass detritus of society, the one with the greatest potential impact is organic waste.

Of the human waste we produce, up to 70 percent can be organic in origin; this leads us back to the soil. Soil, of necessity, is the point of engagement.

In many instances, the quantity of organic waste available may not be sufficient to match the soil quality requirements for food production. However, the fact that organic waste is produced wherever humanity survives does mean that it can provide a physical and mental connection for the individual and the household back to the soil. Be that in the individual home garden, a community vegetable plot, or the productive soil on a local farm, the ability to connect back to the importance of soils for food production and environmental protection is a very tangible outcome for the community; it can be built upon and developed to facilitate our collective future. It must also be kept in mind that there are many ways to process organic material to produce products of increasing value—but more on that later.

The True Value of Materials

Values in the industries that preside over the wastage of materials have always been biased to favor the larger industries, not the local community. When I started working in the field of recycling in the late 1980s, iron ore was valued at around $30 per ton. Back then, the value of any plastic or metal product in the waste stream was much higher. Iron ore can vary in terms of the percentage of iron that is in the ore. On average it is more than 60 percent, but in any case, it is necessary to use a large amount of energy to separate the iron product from the ore body.

At that same time, a colleague who had not been involved in domestic recycling for long, but who had worked for many years as an engineer in the iron industry, was amused at the arguments being put forward by local governments that recycling was not viable because of the cost of reprocessing. Certainly, there are arguments that go toward the cost of separating one product from another, but as is argued elsewhere in this book, much of the cost of separation can be overcome by having source separation in place at the point where the material is discarded. The sale prices of products can vary widely on the international market, particularly when cheap or slave labor is used to manufacture them. When environmental costs are not taken into consideration, it can be far cheaper in terms of dollar value to buy new products rather than to recycle the old.

It must be kept in mind, however, that under current waste industry standards, any process used to handle products we have wasted has enormous negative environmental effects. The process of landfill, once lauded as the ultimate way to dispose of goods people no longer wanted, was seen as simple and safe—principally because, in the interests of so-called efficiency, the organic fraction was dutifully mixed in with everything else. This ensured 100 percent contamination, and communities had to bury it all for health reasons. Now, however, as we begin to count the methane production and atmospheric damage, the cost of liners, the replacement cost, the cost of leaks, and the effects on local housing and health, this method is clearly far from safe. The capture of methane from this process is generally unmeasured, unquantified, and unknown in cost. Yet this bizarre and clearly unworkable, environmentally harmful process is not only praised but is rewarded.

The only reason landfills generate methane is because the materials we put in them contain a high percentage of organic material. Yet organic material, if returned to agriculture and soils, is one of the most valuable materials any household or business discards—in fact, it is the most valuable. The value of organic products like manure, food, straw, and sawdust is enormous in terms of food production for a remote community supported by subsistence farming over a period of several thousand years. In such a community, one hectare of productive land, supported by animal manure, crop stubble, cover crops, and good management, would be of far greater value than any great piece of fine art in any auction house around the world at any time in history. Such a piece of land would have sustained and fed hundreds, if not thousands, of generations of one community, and as such is irreplaceable. But it may not have achieved this result without external organic inputs—namely the manure and other products and sensible biological management. In addition to any other values, it should be remembered that any ton of material diverted from landfill has already saved the community the cost of that ton going to landfill and the cost of replacing that cubic meter of space in a future landfill.

So, if all of this seems to benefit the individual community, what makes change so difficult? There are a number of factors—not the least of which are the very large profits being made by large companies from the management of others' waste. How do very large—often foreign—

companies influence the way services are provided and the way profits are distributed? They do what many large companies with interest in chemicals, fertilizer, weapons, fossil fuels, mining, and manufacturing do: they use whatever means they can to influence decision makers.

A very good example of this is the artificial crisis created by China's refusal in 2017 to accept any more mixed waste products being sold to them as recycled materials. Both the waste industry and other governments immediately began to cry in the media about the need for massive injections of funds to solve the problem. In my local area, the government of New South Wales announced an additional $47 million for local governments to help with recycling. How, you might ask, would this help when nothing had changed? No different collection process, no different handling systems, no different outcomes—just a huge splurge into the pockets of local government and existing waste companies to do more of what they had been doing, which was essentially making mash out of valuable materials. A very different outcome might have been achieved if that same amount of money had gone into sending someone to Europe to see why the governments of Germany and Wales had become the best recycling countries in the world, and then to implement some of the findings. Ten of those millions could have been used to establish source-separation trials in New South Wales, and a tender could have been called, once clean source-separated products were guaranteed, to establish a glass reprocessing facility and a plastics reprocessing facility to make local products or, at very least, manufacturing inputs.

Most importantly for Australia, source separation of organic materials could have led to the establishment of new composting plants and to a move to call the states together under the National Product Stewardship Act to ensure all organic material went back to soil as a matter of law, in a range of forms.

When it comes to value for the recycling dollar, we need to decide how we want our rates spent. If we simply want a waste system, where we invest a large amount of money in a bin, a truck, and a hole in the ground, we may as well pile up our waste budget and set fire to it in terms of environmental outcomes. If we want more than that—if we want sound and safe resource management, employment, and a good return on our tax investment, we need to demand that our local authorities do things differently.

The most important decisions on the use of materials comes back to us. It is our material— we have paid for it and we own it, so we need to decide what we want done with it: either jobs and value, or waste and pollution.

Environmental Protection Authorities were established to protect public health against those who treat the environment as a dumping ground and those who, despite regulation, will still try to take advantage of every opportunity to increase their income at the cost of community and environmental health. We need to work with regulators, recognizing that they too need to change some of their structures and increase their knowledge if new programs are to be effective. There is also the danger that environmental regulators are from the same professional group, career interests, and skill range as the waste industry and that the waste industry will apply pressure to ensure any change from their business model is slow and ponderous. Regulators can also become too focused on waste issues and may have little or no knowledge of material applications or alternate uses. In the midst of all this, if your local authority has a manager who is resisting change, community consultation can become perfunctory, focusing principally on covering risk for the people in your local government. Consultants in our area regularly hold public meetings, but despite recorded recommendations, identification of funding grants, and documented needs and wants, little if anything ever happens. So again, change starts with us and our perception of the value for our taxes.

Collections

She then collected all the bits
To which the world she hoped would bind
With all the words she placed the things
Of love—a palace for the blind
and with the songs she placed the strings
To swoon the heart and lift the pride
Of fools and lover's music bound
All sound, secure and alibied

And in the minds of those at loss
She helped to simply join the dots
Of future, past and present
Now—reflected in a flattened tin
A box, a bough, a bag of dreams
A place of rest—the rest of schemes
She gathered all these bits precise
The remnants of paradise

CHAPTER 2
Collections

The method of aggregating anything, be it organics, bottles, papers, clothing, etc., will determine in great part the quality of the gathered material and its end use.

The method of collecting something of minimal value directly impacts the end quality of the material. The terminology for recycling collections and their rationale, in the main, is bogged down in inaccurate words, distorted facts, questionable reports, and a general inability to reach beyond mediocrity. There are communities that have gone beyond the norm, and there are countries such as Germany and Wales that stand out for quality materials collections—but these are disappointingly rare. The notion of waste collections is arguably one of the biggest issues with waste management. The term "waste" and the "recycling of waste" are unfortunately almost interchangeable in the minds of many people in the industry.

The crass and often inaccurate use of the term "sustainable," blended in with environmental inaccuracies and self-serving concepts, means commercial evolution and careful design have been all but abandoned. These concepts blend together to block rational movement toward the inevitable day when we adopt an attitude of protection toward any and all resources, if for no other reason than that they are limited on this relatively small globe in the middle of space. As mentioned elsewhere, the continued existence of humans as animals on a planet where nature operates a system that has no waste means that we must eventually agree to operate under nature's zero waste system or cease to exist.

Container deposits are a good example of how concepts can be distorted and dismembered by well-meaning intent. Many years ago, prior to the development of the throwaway economy and waste management systems, common practice decreed that all containers and material used as packaging or to construct packages were so valued and valuable as to warrant care and protection in their use, recovery and reuse. Bottles especially were routinely reused time and time again. The advent of the disposable container and the aggressive profiteers who churned them out resulted in extensive litter, which in turn resulted in dramatic alterations to the highly valued beer bottle and milk bottle recovery process. Beer and milk bottles circulated through the economy because of their fundamental necessity as a distribution system of two very important products. It was not that long ago that beer was consumed because it was a far safer way to drink water than water itself. The recovery and resale of beer bottles was part of the total system.

The introduction of disposables and the rapid reduction in value and cost meant that these bottles were disposed of as litter. This resulted in some areas developing a new pre-costed version of the beer bottle recovery system to reduce and control this litter for the ongoing benefit of disposable container producers. This was a new system that was predicated on litter reduction and recovery—and on the aversion to what was perceived as waste on the streets. This recovery system was focused on very few containers—mainly those of a few large companies who supported the system because it improved their public image. It meant that any container included in the new container deposit system had an additional cost applied to the product at the point of sale, which the customer paid for and which was recovered if the container was returned.

In the midst of all this, however, the range of materials produced as packaging—including plastics, paper, cardboard, aluminum, steel, and glass—grew exponentially and extravagantly. A very small and limited number of these packaging materials, mainly structured around small portable soft drink and beer containers, became the focus of the anti-litter campaign of container deposits and rode into history as one of the great recycling panaceas of Western society. Today these stand-alone recovery systems operate in very few countries and only gather about 1.5 percent of total waste, unless they are connected to a community center that adds more value and more comprehensive processes. In other areas, where container deposits did not necessarily apply, materials of consistent value such as paper and cardboard were being collected to raise funds for clubs and community service organizations. The steel-can drink market made way for the highly-valued aluminum one, and these cans were readily collected for their value. Why aluminum, originally developed to support new lightweight aircraft, was ever used for disposable drink cans is a question that should be brought up to the World Environment and Intentional Pollution Court, whenever we manage to get one established. Such a court is needed to protect the planet against human ignorance and greed.

These ad hoc collections eventually led to more coordinated aggregation processes in which more and more materials were marketed for reuse and recycling as their values were realized.

After many communities started operating drop-off facilities, some began to plan door-to-door collections. Even then, there were few in the recycling world who appreciated that carefully collected materials could create local value, jobs, and products.

In many parts of the world, collections ran ahead of infrastructure and reprocessing ability, and the speed and efficiency used to collect waste was transferred to the new recycling boon. Contracted collectors in Australia used the same people and methods for collecting recycling crates that they had for waste. These containers were initially blue when used in their earlier iteration in Seattle. Waste was often collected by fit, young men who ran from one house to the next—the big claim was most waste collections were over by lunch time. The same speed, when applied to recycling, combined with a reluctance to take trucks back to the depot for emptying, resulted in over-stuffed vehicles and many heavy glass containers being accidently thrown through car windows or smashed on footpaths. It was common before the era of Occupational Health and Safety to see a collection worker on a 3-meter-high pile of glass bottles in the back of a truck being thrown a full 55-liter crate from the roadway. The result was the arrival of the less-labor-intensive side loader in the recycling world.

Collection Trials

In 1992 I was engaged to run the educational and engagement aspects of the collection trials run in Canberra, Australia, with what at the time was an eye-watering $1.4 million budget to evaluate all the recycling methods then in use around the world. This included bags, crates, small wheeled bins, and large 240-liter wheeled bins. In the interest of neatness and efficiency we decided on bins, using combinations of 120-, 140-, and 240-liter sizes, some with dividers to collect glass as separate from paper; glass with plastics, separate from paper; 240-liter bins divided left to right with paper at the rear; and other configurations. Toward the end of this trial we were operating seven system variations in five different areas. The truck driver was issued a color-coded chart ordered by collection type and date. This showed him what type of gear he needed to put on or take off the truck for collections that particular day. When these first commenced, we were using a divided truck that had a noisy but effective lifting conveyor. It delivered a mostly unbroken product, but it was slow and therefore inefficient. The speed of the lifter could not keep up with the speed of the truck. The divided bins, using a side loader, could dump into two areas at once. Other bins had to be lifted separately and emptied into the correct truck section.

The difficulty with these systems was that they were fixated on the use of side-loader vehicles. With side-loader vehicles comes the ultimate temptation of compaction, which increases efficiency by reducing the need to return to base to empty the truck. In a situation in which one contractor was doing the collection and another was doing the separation at a MRF, there was a clear conflict of interest: the collector was trying to maximize the material on the truck, but the more this happened the poorer the quality of the material collected, and the amount of waste produced went up because the MRF was not designed (nor was it part of the contract) to deal with a high percentage of waste. Side-loader vehicles and quality product are mutually exclusive. The only way to collect material and get good product quality is to collect it carefully—the model researched and used by the government of Wales has demonstrated this over some years.[11] Careful collection has always resulted in cleaner and better-quality product, regardless of

> **Side-loader vehicles and quality product are mutually exclusive. The only way to collect material and get good product quality is to collect it carefully...**

what is picked up. Research undertaken in Wales has proven this to be the best value for the community, creating jobs, products, clean organic waste, and electricity through anaerobic digestion, with the residual organic product going out to farm soils.

Crucial to such programs is community engagement. The importance of getting the community fully involved in any recycling program cannot be overstated. People must see their part clearly, and they must also be able to understand that the issues are far more than simply recycling materials. They must be able to see from the outset that they, the human component, are the most important element of the program. The engagement strategy used must reflect trust, conversation and excitement. Most importantly, people need to understand why they are involved. While this may seem somewhat esoteric and mystical, it is a very simple message that people clearly understand.

The first Canberra program I was involved in was in the suburb of Kaleen. The engagement strategy with the community was the fact that they were pioneers in the program. A survey conducted in four

---

11. "Local Authority Municipal Waste Management: October to December 2018," accessed 5 July, 2019, https://gov.wales/local-authority-municipal-waste-management-october-december-2018/.

areas in the suburb midway through the trial demonstrated the success of the strategy of seeking felt personal involvement. Households were requested to mail back their response to the survey and to provide their opinion of what could be done to improve the collections program. The response rate was 55 percent, which was unheard of in the days before the general internet. The trial ran for two years, and the materials collected were taken to a very small MRF where they were sorted into categories by hand and sent to market. We collected vast amounts of information, including many personal experiences of frustration, misunderstanding, humor, and correction during the trial.

One peculiarity that generated a note of hilarity was the attitude of households to the collection of their waste. It had become a tradition in Australia to provide beer at Christmas to waste collectors as a "Thank you" for services provided. Some people continued this tradition despite the fact that the truck was a side loader and the bin was not physically handled by the operator. People would place donations of aluminum cans of beer into their bins, under the closed lid. The full beer cans of course tumbled around in the collection truck all the way to the MRF, then emptied out into a hopper. There was always broken glass in with the beer cans, and by the time they appeared with other recyclables on the belt for processing, the cans all contained many pin holes, with shaken beer was spraying out of them like miniature Greek fountains.

After two years of comprehensive research, wheeled 240-liter bins were provided to all homes with yards in Canberra, while high-rise homes were given larger hoppers. The program was rolled out in 1994 and was initially operated by the US firm Browning Ferris Industries (BFI). BFI managed both collections and the MRF—a regrettable plan for all parties involved. The company had made the government an offer so cheap it would not be refused. The result was that BFI lost money on the contract when material prices began to fall internationally.

This was my first personal experience of how the collection method was directly related to the quality output of the system. Also, as time went on, the amount of money spent on education and product quality both fell in real terms. Australia's national capital has a large itinerant population and the total exchange of people around those years was 8 percent per annum. Continuous engagement and education to keep any program running smoothly is crucial. People cannot learn by osmosis—they must be engaged and at least kept interested. Every year, potentially 8 percent of the population had less of an idea of how or if the system worked. It is arguable that twenty-five years after introduction of the concept to the community it would be falling apart at the seams—and, in terms of quality, it is. In a system in which little care is taken with quality, where conceptually the notion of separation of products is left to the worst stage of the process, requiring mechanical rather than human engagement, a program becomes a public relations farce and a recycling disaster. The processes associated with recycling, in combination with the concept that we live on a resource-limited planet, must be partnered in an evolutionary process.

People must understand why they are doing something. Knowing that they put materials into a bin and placing it on the street are the what and the how—but they have nothing to do with the why.

Side-loader collection vehicles will be the death of recycling in many communities if the only considerations are price, speed, and the nuanced concept that recycling is happening. Side-loader compactor vehicles lead to a waste collection system that is as far removed from the careful, quality collections of Wales as it is possible to be. Enthusiasts of resource conservation and protection often make the point that the priority should be not so much on the provision of "end of pipe" solutions as on waste avoidance, reuse, and recycling—in that order. However, such a policy position does not necessarily identify the difficulties associated with value-added collection nor the circumstances in which it is done. Nor does it consider that the average household, eating a reasonable diet and preparing most meals from scratch, will produce around two liters of organic waste per day. Unless you want them to stop eating, this output will be continuous. The output will be matched by packaging, and because of this we need a collections process—not for "waste" but for materials. Have a container deposit if you must, but put it on everything, because the most valuable part of this material, as I shall demonstrate elsewhere, is the organic fraction.

It is utterly crucial to include the "why" elements, because as you move around the world, different criteria operate in different communities. Varied community standards and values determine the hierarchical position of the collector/processor and the value of the materials/goods to the local community. However, the locals will always need to know why they are doing it.

It should be clear by now that the method of collecting any material from a house or business fundamentally determines the quality, and therefore the value, of the product to the end user or processor.

If organic material contains broken glass, pieces of plastic, or any other contaminant, it can dramatically reduce the value of the product. Clean product cannot be produced by a MRF—it is physically impossible, despite the enthusiasm of engineers who might insist they can sort fly dirt from ground pepper. Even if they could, by collecting mixed materials, the system is missing the opportunity to engage the community in the why of the process and will continue to collect mixed product—i.e., waste.

There are many examples of diverse collection processes, and we shall discuss the implications for the end use of several of them. Please remember that my experience as retold here is just that—while I have seen a lot of collection systems at work in many different countries, by no means have I seen them all. There are few who have—so it is important to remember that there are often local reasons for collection methodologies. For example, food waste and yard waste are collected separately in some parts of the world. In Australia, however, due to issues of distribution and soil quality, it makes more sense to collect both organic streams—food and garden organics—in one bin. There are also examples of different organic processes that add considerable value to the end product that I shall explain in detail elsewhere. However, as a general point, the separation of materials from each other and a lack of compaction will mean higher quality and value. As the production of household waste and its component parts have changed over the years, collection systems have as well. Demand for recycling programs and the protection of human health have also supposedly been instrumental in the use of varied containers and vehicles, both human-powered and motorized. There are some instances in which change could be instrumental in improving both human wealth and health.

Some Other Parts of the World

A very good example of an alternate system was the development of a training session that Mal Williams of the Zero Waste International Trust and I conducted with the Zabbaleen people in Cairo, Egypt.[12] The focus of the training session was an inoculant-based process we refined in Australia for upcycling composted organic materials. The Zabbaleen are Coptic Christian farmers who came to Cairo in the late 1940s after a severe drought had hit rural areas. Around that time, they commenced collecting waste (then mostly food waste) from households and used it to feed their pigs—their principle farming occupation.

Today, collections are conducted every day but the Sabbath, with the price of collection varying depending on the area of the city and the arrangement between the collector and the household. The collected materials—dry recyclables and wet organics—are taken back to family or community sites in various parts of the city, and the organic materials are separated from the bottles, cans, and plastics. Organic materials are fed to pigs once they are separated from other waste. Over many years, the Zabbaleen developed manual and mechanical systems

---

12. "In Cairo's Garbage City, These Entrepreneurs Could Be the World's Best Recyclers" by Elizabeth MacBride, Forbes website, published 8 January, 2017, https://www.forbes.com/sites/elizabethmacbride/2017/01/08/in-cairos-garbage-city-the-lure-of-profits-is-strong-so-are-the-mothers/#476aaca81c39/.

for handling most forms of other materials in their own communities. They produce paper, cardboard, and clean, pelletized plastic products for resale. The rest of the world could learn a great deal from them.

Our involvement was focused on an issue that had developed in 2009 when the Mubarak government ordered 350,000 pigs killed because of the threat of the swine flu epidemic. This was the total stock of Zabbaleen-owned pigs, and it was a bitter blow to them. Many believed that the destruction of their pigs was related to political and religious beliefs rather than swine flu. In any case, the net result was that the organic waste previously consumed by the pigs was immediately of no value to the Zabbaleen. It was left in the streets, with a resultant increase in rats and other vermin and, of course, an increased potential for rapid spread of disease.

Our role was to demonstrate alternative processes to restore value to the collected food wastes. We used the City to Soil system I designed for use in Australia to engage households in organic collections. The City to Soil program encourages source separation at the household and an effective system of composting that reduces odor by using an inoculant. This was easily transferable into the Cairo situation. The Gates Foundation provided funds for the project to the Zabbaleen group Spirit of Youth via an organization called Hands Along the Nile. It was a project initiated by the NGO sector's friend in Cairo, Goldman Prize winner Dr. Laila Iskander,[13] who had been appointed Environment Minister by the interim government prior to the election of President Sisi.

Hands Along the Nile had found that the separation by hand of organic waste from other collected materials by Zabbaleen families was a very big health issue to the family members doing the work. They were interested in developing a program to help the families separate the food waste into compostable bags and to use that material in compost processes. They wanted us to demonstrate the making of the odor-controlling inoculant and to follow that with a two-day course

---

13. Laila Iskandar," accessed 5 July, 2019, https://www.goldmanprize.org/recipient/laila-iskandar-kamel/.

on the making of compost. On our first visit to Cairo we provided the instructions on inoculant manufacturing. On the second, when we were to provide training on making compost, it proved very hard—or at least very expensive—to find the raw materials. So, to proceed with the composting demonstration, we used a mixture of food-contaminated paper waste and pig manure in a balanced carbon-to-nitrogen ratio. Since that time, the Zabbaleen have gone back to using pigs as their processor of choice for organic waste. We are not sure if the inoculant and compost process continues to be used, and we have not been able to check on the situation due to the instability of the political circumstances in Cairo. We were told that one of the more interesting aspects of pig production for the Zabbaleen was that their families ate less than 10 percent of the pork. The rest went out to the community, who unlike the Zabbaleen are not, in the main, Christian.

The Zabbaleen are unusual in that they have been waste collectors in Cairo for over seventy years. From time to time, other waste companies from other parts of the world have been induced or contracted by the government and others to collect waste in the city, but few last long. The Zabbaleen door-to-door collection service is unique in that it captures all domestic waste and in that its recovery levels for recycling are extremely high—around 85 percent—and therefore very effective. Apart from removing organic waste, very large quantities of other materials such as plastics and cardboard are processed and returned to the market. Many of the building spaces under family homes contain a range of machinery that is processing resources back to their original state for resale into the world market. Naturally, in non-regulated processing areas such as Cairo, there are instances where health and safety have become an issue. Injuries are not uncommon. Having said that, the methods of the Zabbaleen in processing plastics back into pellets for sale to the market are an example to any community wishing to establish its own processes.

Family accidents and general circumstance can sometimes mean that children are orphaned, and the Zabbaleen must look after their own community members. Also, schooling in some areas is such that children, who are working, need to incorporate their education into their working lives. To facilitate this, the Zabbaleen have developed their own Recycling School, which provides education to children who are working almost full time. Procter and Gamble were finding that some unscrupulous individuals in Egypt were refilling their shampoo bottles with a range of soap and water and selling it in the streets as shampoo. To overcome this, they provided funds to the Recycling School to capture their specific bottle waste and shred it to prevent refills. This Procter and Gamble material was then cleaned and sold to the world market as pelletized plastic. The children brought their Proctor and Gamble products to the Recycling School, where they were weighed, shredded, cleaned, baled, and again weighed for sale. To manage all this, the school children had to use the school's computers for their individual business accounts, which meant they needed to use two Microsoft programs, Excel and Word. The net result was children with successful recycling businesses who could write and speak in both Arabic and English and operate their own business accounts. They could also explain the structure and operation of their business in clear and concise English. In many other countries this would have been regarded as child labor; in this instance however, it gave the children business skills, mathematical knowledge, and management abilities in two languages—written and spoken.

Not only do the Zabbaleen keep Cairo functioning and reasonably disease free by managing its wastes— they also provide income, education, and a healthy diet for their families and meat for the larger population. It is a very big win for all parts of the community from a comprehensive recycling program.

The wealth generated from the waste streams of Cairo stay in Cairo for the benefit of the entire community.

Another example of community engagement and health and wealth from recycling comes from the other side of the world, in Raglan, New Zealand. Commencing in 1998, as a community-based recycler, Xtreme Zero Waste is a community-owned operation that uses business as a tool to meet the needs of its community.[14] The organization is contracted by the local Waikato District Council and the Raglan Resource Recovery Centre to operate weekly curbside collections at what used to be the local landfill and is now a transfer station. They have achieved consistently high levels of diversion from landfill and are turning Raglan's waste into resources for community employment and environmental benefit, while moving toward zero waste.

The original landfill for Raglan was established in the 1950s beside the Te Hutewai valley. This meant that there was always a possibility of leachate from the landfill flowing into the stream, Whaingaroa Harbour, and the estuary system. In 1998 the landfill was closed and a transfer station was established. Landscaping of the site commenced, and trees were planted over the old landfill. Following a number of meetings, the community began researching alternatives to landfill. In that same year, a wetland was developed by Whaingaroa Harbour Care, with filtration ponds above it. This ensured that any leachate from the old landfill would have to pass through the set of ponds maintained by Xtreme Waste before it got to the wetland. The system they developed means that by the time the leachate from the old landfill reaches the harbor, the toxicity will be depleted to the point where contamination is unable to be detected in the water by the local Regional Council.

In 1999 a local educational trust, Whakamaua-te-Aio, commenced management of green waste and took over paper and cardboard recycling. They also developed a business plan and budget for a zero-waste strategy. The trust was committed to advocating for zero waste in Raglan and working proactively with the Raglan community to achieve the goal. By 2001 they had achieved a diversion rate of 74

---

14. Xtreme Zero Waste website, accessed 5 July, 2019, http://xtremezerowaste.org.nz/.

percent and Xtreme Waste was providing additional services through business collections and rural pick-ups. They also offered waste audits to businesses to demonstrate potential savings from recycling. By 2009 they had introduced street bins managed by Xtreme Waste, and the amount to landfill was further reduced. The same year, turnover for the business, which had only been in operation for ten years, reached over $1 million. That same year they launched Para Kore—"zero waste"—to minimize waste in traditional Maori indigenous marae (villages). The business has provided mentoring to forty-six other groups in New Zealand establishing similar operations. Their diversion rate now runs consistently close to 80 percent as they continue their tree-planting program and the control of feral animals on their site.

Engagement

At the other extreme, most of the government agencies I have worked with and for in Australia have little faith in the household-er. In Canberra we had the population very excited when curbside recycling started. We made sure during the trial period that all vehicles carried logos to show who we were. We communicated through a regular newsletter, and staff working on a daily basis with the community in the suburbs were encouraged to stop and have conversations in the street or a cup of tea with homeowners. Right through the trial period the excitement was maintained, and the community was enthusiastic. However, after the full program across the national capital was introduced in 1994, this excitement quickly waned. The process became "normal," engagement budgets were minimized, and the staff changed. The public's attitude became moribund with disinterest.

The engagement program dropped from being our principal objective into an education project that has now faded, except for material, sent out if and when people ask for it, and occasional school visits to the MRF. Also, the objective when I was involved in the original recycling trials in 1992 was simply to recycle bulk material—we were very wrong at the time in regard to quality, and this continues to be a problem. I had looked into the use of pedestrian-controlled vehicles and a "sort direct to vehicle" program—something I had learned about from sources in the UK—but this never got very far in Australia because of the influence of industry in maintaining the current system. By that time, they were aware of the fact that they were paid with side-loaders to collect and partially compact, and then also paid to disassemble; the result, of course, is higher cost and a lower-quality product. An exception to this in Canberra today is curbside organics collection, in which the operator has an individual who handles engagement and is always out in public talking to people, with a focus on quality. The result thus far in collections is almost no contamination.

This has also happened with the City to Soil program, where preventing and reducing contamination is reliant not only on the system but also on the people who deliver it and the manner in which they talk to the community. We now have one good example of City to Soil in Armidale, New South Wales. This program flourishes because of the people who run the program and the way they engage the community. They are determined to give the public a high-quality compost product because the people give them clean organics to start with. In other councils with similar programs, interest has waned because there was no one to maintain public support. The excitement created by a successful program, such as Armidale's City to Soil, which wins awards and saves money, keeps the community focused. This has likewise happened in Wales, where the excitement is created in part by the shift from 5 percent recycling in 1999 to over 60 percent today. This is not far behind the recycling level in Germany, the world leader, and I have no doubt that many of the 350 European zero-waste communities are also reflecting this substantial shift. Many municipalities in the EU are over 80 percent now.[15]

The spectacular rise of recycling in Wales is driven by a sincere focus on citizen engagement so that the householder presents the materials for professional curbside collection separately one from the other. The program recognizes that to achieve 100 percent high-quality

---

14. "Our Network," Zero Waste Europe website, accessed 5 July, 2019, https://zerowasteeurope.eu/our-network/.

materials, everyone must be recycling 100 percent of their materials 100 percent of the time. This is the basis of the Zero Waste Policy, which keeps Wales focused on its direction. It's a good policy, but the addition of internal markets, local use of organics, and a desire to improve makes it an excellent one. Crucially, it is strategically driven by the statutory duty placed on the Welsh Government to promote sustainable development. An analysis in terms of cost savings has also reflected extraordinary change in public perception and government interest. The good news stories affect future plans.

Well-managed collections in Wales have demonstrated that custom-designed, multi-compartmented Resource Recovery Vehicles (RRVs), into which dry recyclables and food wastes are directly sorted when collected each week from every household, produces the best results. In fact, these vehicles are regarded as fundamental. They work in partnership with a distributed network of simple sorting and bulking facilities throughout the country, allowing local handling of high-quality products directly to market. Wales has a Collections Blueprint that has been adopted by an increasing number of its 22 local authorities.[16] More will be joining as the benefits become obvious. This means that curbside sort collections are becoming standard across Wales, with corresponding benefits for procurement and the raising of awareness, along with all the other community outcomes.

Due to a focus on source separation and the quality of materials that are collected, several companies are looking to invest in Wales.

The local governments ("Blueprint Authorities") that are using the collection system are making big financial savings, both due to the efficiency of the operations and because they can command good prices

---

14. Best Practice in High Diversion," Collections Blueprint Wales website, accessed 5 July, 2019, https://collectionsblueprint.wales/.

for their high-quality materials. These same authorities are also making significant additional contributions to reducing carbon impacts.

Some of the factors that have contributed to progress in Wales include:

- Mandatory collection of dry recyclables
- Mandatory separate collection of bio waste
- Statutory recycling targets
- Reduction of residual waste
- Statutory overall waste reduction
- Landfill taxes—to improve the economic argument for recycling
- Recommendation for curbside-sorted collections
- Reduced frequency of residual waste collections
- Reduced size of residual waste collection bins
- Committed long-term funding, underpinned by an ambitious strategy
- Targeted investment and technical assistance via the Collaborative Change Programme

Wales has developed a behavior-change campaign that has three basic pillars: communications, service provision, and enforcement. After implementation of the government's initial recycling efforts, an analysis revealed that half of the material left in residual waste containers was recyclable. The objective to become the leading recycler in the world meant that they needed to recover around 50 percent of that material. To achieve this, the government instituted a public relations campaign to encourage people to believe that recycling is the normal thing to do. In other words, "if you are not recycling, you should be." It was argued that such a focus would enable government to engage sports people, musicians, and other artist and artisans to tell the people of Wales, "You are the best in the world—well done!"

The experience in Wales has been that handing out brochures and leaflets has little impact. The very real impact occurs because the system works. When people see that it works and are engaged in the process, they participate and become more involved. For those who don't, there is always regulation and enforcement; however, the argument is that if it's normal to recycle—an activity that produces clean products and improved sales and jobs—people will get behind the process. And producing waste and being a person who doesn't recycle will become about as popular as smokers in restaurants. The Wales model will progressively bring in more regulation to underpin its true goal: zero waste by 2050. As in other communities, the Wales Zero Waste target was originally seen as ridiculous—but it is now government policy. Stories abound of people from all segments of Welsh society who can and do recycle. Even those with little in life are motivated and engaged in recycling. Sustainable development needs to be seen as a wide-ranging concept that people will embrace as they see it successfully implemented in their daily lives.

In the larger picture, the Welsh government views its engagement with civil society, and the structure of reuse and recycling as a tool to support that engagement, as a means of delivering broader social benefits. An example is FRAME in Pembrokeshire, which delivers necessary recycling and reuse services to the local community while at the same time providing employment and training to disabled members of the community. This broader focus will help Wales use recycling as a mechanism to create benefits way beyond the environment and the national economy, and to build recycling and reuse strategies into a national framework.

Such examples highlight the importance international organizations, such as the Zero Waste International Alliance, Ecocycle Solutions, and Zero Waste Europe, to help local communities. These organization can help those individual communities determine where they wish to go and what they wish to achieve and can help them follow the zero-waste road.

CHAPTER 3
Panaceas and Plastic Bags

The ability to recognize that all of nature is interconnected has been fundamental to the survival of all indigenous communities. In our modern economy, however, a reductionist approach to science has isolated specialist knowledge into specific fields of endeavor, with cross-pollination of scientific abilities either dismissed or actively discouraged.

There is little awareness at any level of the population that the quality of the environment, specifically the quality of soil, in many ways determines not only the quantity and quality of water but also the quality of human health. We are, after all, what we eat.

The civilizations that have survived flood, drought, disease, and famine are those that have a reliable, high-quality, and consistent food supply. Those with a successful agrarian base are the ones that nurture their soils, caring not only for the plants and their interactions with animals above the ground but also for the biology of the soil, which stimulates the release of nutrients and maintains soil structure, secures carbon, and retains moisture. This in turn increases land value.

Within this context, the concept of waste becomes a metaphor for our attitude to the planet on which we rely for our survival. This is our approach in so many fields that we have become a panacea population, soothed by placebo effects. For most of our social ills we provide more ambulances at the bottom of the cliff rather than install or repair the fence at the top. In our legal system we build more jails rather than spend money on the social issues that create the problems. This same jail system supposedly deals with anti-social behavior, which may well have been addressed with a better-resourced education system or an alternate engagement system for those who do breach the law. Social alienation is often the cause of social behavior, which leads to a prison sentence, which is then addressed by further alienation in prisons.

We seem to have difficulty coming to terms with the need for change, even when it is to our overall social benefit. We treat these problems as hysterical political issues, which means that we usually create an even more difficult symptom, which in turn requires even more investment, and so on, to the bottom of the cliff. In providing urban housing accommodation we have the ability to design structures that use little or no external energy, yet we build poorly and then retrofit them with air conditioning and heating at enormous social and environmental cost.

Our "end of pipe" attitude is reflected in our health and education as well. In our "developed" populations we cannot in all truth refer to our system of community care as a health system since its principal focus is on keeping people alive once they are ill. We spend the vast majority of money on preventing sick people from dying, not on keeping people well. This is not a health system at all—it is a death system. We address only the symptoms of our disease. Health specialists and doctors in China spend more time and public money keeping people healthy than curing ills. This seemingly obvious—and, by our standards, pragmaticapproach—results in a health system focused on the best interests of both the community and the individual. This old but effective health system was historically reflected back to the origin of the population's food supply, which is the soil.

Waste, like illness, incarceration, and ignorance, is the result of a lack of care, and a lack of care is reflected in our attitudes to consumption. The structure of human values within Western society is bordered by parameters such as new or old, antique or second hand, used, reused, and recycled. In most modern economies, up-and-coming younger generations, in many instances, pursue the new in preference to the old—they must have the latest in all things. Asset gain is the principal social imperative. The driver is "more"; to have "more" is to be happy. More money equals more things, and more things equals more happiness.

Our modern social context is predicated on getting what you want—not necessarily what you need. The corporate intent of the commercial world is to spread that same condition to the rest of humanity so that every human on earth can also get what they want and not necessarily what they need.

This does not occur due to any interest in social justice or fairness or equity, but simply to ensure that the shareholders' investment in the corporate structure is constantly protected by new markets and more profit for vested interests. In the creation of these new markets the only obligation of both the corporate structure and its board of directors is to make more money for the shareholder. The shareholders in turn are comfortably removed from the day-to-day liabilities and any ethical responsibility for the behavior of the directors by simply declaring that their interests are purely an investment.

Despite the way our economy is structured, if individuals were made fully aware of the environmental destruction caused by shareholder interests and consumptive society, would they continue to support it? Environmental groups constantly question this model, which is clearly eating the heart out of our potential to exist on the planet. Yet we battle to stop it. Indeed, Western lifestyle in the main supports and encourages the very consumption that is clearly destroying it. We have taken the Industrial Revolution to its logical consumptive conclusion by driving the principal valued resources of the planet toward zero and raising pollution levels to the maximum. Yet the 2009 financial collapse, driven by greed, was immediately followed by huge investment by governments around the world, using community money to support the very system that created the cancer in the first place.

What we have just seen occur will occur again unless we drive change from a different position. We need a base for our economy other than profit. We need to go beyond treating only the symptoms of our disease. We are told that we need consumption as a part of our economic condition. To expand a healthy economy we must have profits, and to maintain profits we must consume. This is woven into every part of the global economy, and it is the principal mantra of political life on the advice of economic principals founded in the Industrial Revolution. This mantra in turn is driven by the tools of Wall Street, the World Bank, and the World Monetary Fund, for the financial benefit of a small minority of wealthy individuals.

Being new is a state of being, a position in a continuum—a role in a phase of life that is not more or less important than any other. It simply is. It is a secondary element of birth itself. It is a place where all things are at one time. It is not something to be retained at all cost—it is simply a phase through which all things must pass on their continuing journey to the next. Yet achievement of the state of "new" in all things is the consumer's principal icon.

In the environmental movement, most of our efforts in developing recycling tools do little more than replicate and endorse the very technology that made the destructive product socially desirable in the first place. Our personal guilt in engaging in the pursuit of greed and in using the materials of our age is assuaged by our efforts to help the corporate world reclaim their assets at highly discounted costs.

We assist metal companies in their recycling programs through the cheap labor of children and service clubs. We give back steel and glass at a fraction of the price we paid for it. We provide newspapers and their editors the tools to continue their economic fabrications by giving them back, at discount prices, the same cheap fiber on which they gave us the questionable information in the first place. What we are currently creating is surely not change but a minor shift in emphasis, a small charity bowl at the end of the profit pipeline.

We might ask if our recycling programs, while creating some social good, have we created any real social shift. The work we do is fiddling on the periphery of the corporate structure. We simply provide some of the means to ensure the slide to the bottom continues, unimpeded by the limitations of conscience. In the process of developing recycling programs, it is true that we have developed many new employment positions and generated great wealth. But have we created real change? While we endorse and indeed support the work of activists such as Vandana Shiva[17] in challenging the movements by the corporate world to own the very means of life itself, our actions as environmental activists in the main support the pursuit of what is wanted rather than what is needed.

Vandana Shiva's work is focused on the fact that many of the farmers she fights for already had most of what they needed before the wealth of Wall Street moved into their backyard. They had what they needed for many generations. She is fighting for the right of her fellow patriots not to have what our corporate structure says they should want. Many farmers in Southeast Asia, India, and Africa have battled to retain their personal connection to their soil. Their reliance on ancient practices has not been shaken by the false promises of the Green Revolution[18] or the threat of an ensuing GM assault on their farms. Indeed, the actions of these farmers, using simple processes in pursuing their biological methods of farming, demonstrate that the tools of the corporate structure are clearly not the magic black

---

17. "Vandana Shiva," Wikipedia, accessed 9 July, 2019, https://en.wikipedia.org/wiki/Vandana_Shiva/.
18. "How the Green Revolution Has Failed to Feed Us," Never Ending Food website, accessed 9 July, 2019, http://www.neverendingfood.org/articles/how-the-green-revolution-has-failed-to-feed-us/.

box they purport to be. We are told that the world needs GMOs to feed the growing population, yet the plain and simple figures do not support this argument. At any time in the world there are around one billion people who are suffering from starvation or who are desperate for food. Yet the population in developed civilizations throws away enough food annually to feed around three billion people. It is clearly not a lack of food on the planet that keeps people starving—it is politics and the want of a decent transport and distribution system!

The drive for GMOs is not driven by facts. It is driven by financial greed. The short-term cash wealth of modern corporate existence pales into insignificance when compared with the biological and economic benefit generated by a thousand generations of subsistence farmers, who produce 60 to 70 percent of the world's food. In a truly soil-based economy, one small hectare of productive land over ten generations is worth many times more than a ton of diamonds. With the crippling results of chemicals such as DDT,[19] Thalidomide, and Agent Orange still swirling through the veins of deformed children around the world, the World Bank is being pressed once again to fund a second round of the failed and despotic Green Revolution. The question is surely not how to replace the success of subsistence farmers and their methods but how to endorse and build on millennia of a successful model so that it can work in every community in the world. Can we have farming models that take the organic base of subsistence farming and build upon it to deliver the needs of humanity, while supporting the needs of the planet and its human inhabitants?

Science, Soils, and Social Insanity

Margaret Wertheim, in her book, *Pythagoras' Trousers*, notes that society develops a concept of scientific outcomes that is somewhat different than the reality of science itself. The scientific reality can be distorted by media to suit the overall social perception of the day. This

---

19. "DDT," Wikipedia, accessed 9 July, 2019, https://en.wikipedia.org/wiki/DDT/.

notion of massed humanity takes the outcome of scientific work and then modifies it to suit what the collective mass thinks it ought to mean. An excellent example of this is the work of Justus von Liebig, who in the 1840s gave us, among his work on chemistry and other matters, the notion of NPK (nitrogen-phosphorus-potassium) fertilizer values. Von Liebig deduced that plant ash contained all the nutrition necessary for plant growth. This of course was later disproved and conceded as inaccurate by Von Liebig himself. Before his death, however, the idea was picked up by others and became the great panacea for future agriculture. Not because it was true, but because it turned a profit for the gun runners and chemical manufacturers from two world wars. Von Liebig was not experienced in agriculture; he in fact boasted of his detachment from such matters. His initial work, however, became the basis for modern industrial farming practices throughout the world.

The principal driver of modern conventional farming developed more from the need of the corporate sector to continue selling the outputs of munitions factories when war ended than from the desire to feed and clothe the world. Chemical manufacturers found that the same chemistry used in weapons could be applied to agriculture. Even if feeding the hungry was the original intent, this certainly has not happened. The powerful position of chemical manufacturers, who determine the focus of research funding in much of the scientific world, is determined by this same financial imperative. They set the agenda, and their corporate partners confirm it for the masses, who often have neither the information nor the ability to refute the considerable data they are given, nor the good sense to challenge the inevitability of their situation. For the past one hundred years we have been sold a story for the production of food in a modern Western economy that is both destructive and cynical, while simultaneously profitable and protective of its corporate base.

But the pressure this corporate model has placed on the resources of the earth is ringing its own death knell. The overuse of phosphate fertilizer has now brought us to a point where at current usage rates we will simply run out of mineable phosphate within thirty years.

The chemical destruction of soils has also resulted in the UN distributing a Scientific American report[20] that says that chemical agriculture has around sixty harvests left before it simply runs out of soil.

Finding an alternative system is imperative. And as organic and biological farmers the world over have been telling us for millennia, an alternative is indeed available. In addition, we now have the necessary means to bring this message to the individual consumer.

The Organic Base

Every individual, regardless of social standing, produces organic waste. The true value of this product in terms of its nutrient value, its ability to feed biology, and its usefulness as a catalyst for the soil has never truly been capitalized on in Western society. Only in Asian communities has any true value of returning organic materials to the soil been appreciated and developed. From death comes life—nature needs the old to make the new.

At the heart of these farming practices is a connection to the food supply and a respect for the soil. Even in Western societies, where the public—with the exception of gardeners—has long been ignorant of the value of this material, a substantial shift has begun to take place with the advent of new programs focused on food. For the first time in its modern history, Western society has begun to truly look at its organic outputs. At first this shift occurred because wasted food is a waste of money; but now, more importantly, it is happening because of the value to the food chain. This in turn has led to a consideration of the value of clean, quality, organic products as catalysts in the production of quality food from quality soil.

---

20. Chris Arsenault, "Only 60 Years of Farming Left If Soil Degradation Continues," Scientific American website, accessed 9 July, 2019, https://www.scientificamerican.com/article/only-60-years-of-farming-left-if-soil-degradation-continues/.

The City to Soil project has clearly demonstrated that given the right tools, motivation, and actionable information, the public will respond enthusiastically to efforts to collect food waste for reuse in soils. This project, using a simple collection system of source separation, has demonstrated that at our very animal base we fully grasp the importance of soil as our mother, in the sense that it feeds and clothes us and our children. As individuals, parents, and grandparents, we see that the security of future generations is firmly based in the soil. The response to this project has seen the collections of organic waste with extremely low contamination rates—less than half of one percent. This project has clearly demonstrated that the public wants to be involved. Indeed, it has demonstrated that the collection of organic waste, once it is embraced by the community, will not only empower them to become part of the solution but will also provide the basis for a link into a much bigger picture of behavioral change.

Compost and Carbon

In developing the City to Soil process, the project managers needed to reduce the cost of compost manufacturing. So, they refined several older compost systems into one in which the organic waste requires no shredding and very little turning. Importantly, this process also produces no odor. Material is sprayed with water and a biological inoculant, covered with tarpaulins, and left for six weeks without turning. The material, as in other aerobic compost processes, can achieve temperatures in excess of 70°C (158°F) in the first week. It then settles back to around 55°C (131°F) for the remainder of the process.[21] The material produced in this compost process, returned to the soil, provides the basis for land management change that can dramatically reduce fertilizer use, improve moisture retention in soils, increase yield, and increase soil carbon. If the legacy emissions currently in the atmosphere are to be addressed, improving our soils worldwide might be

---

21. SPICE compost process – gerrygillespie.net

the only way to do it. While climate change may be the largest threat we have brought upon humanity, the generation of carbon in agricultural soils and the opportunities for change that it brings could be one of the greatest benefits that humanity has ever given back to the world.

We have at our fingertips the means to end poverty, the means to feed the world, and the means for a new world economy. This new direction, this new hope, is based on the simplest and most disregarded of the products of humanity—our organic outputs.

Source-separated organic waste provides the tools to link the community back to its food supply. It provides the tools for us to rebuild our relationship with our soils and the means to support local regional economies. The only thing we need to do to be part of this great revolution is to maintain ownership of our own organic waste.

The global economy has forgotten that we can't have a laborer in China make cheap goods for the world market without food. And we can't feed that laborer without soil. The global economy has forgotten that it is nothing without soil. Every cheap tool, every cheap car, every cheap television represents some part of a nation's soil. We are nothing without soil. Soil creates the very basis of economic value. We can't exist without it. Peak phosphorus spells the death of chemical agriculture. There is a new way. There is a better way—for humanity and for the planet. Owning your organic wastes in your home and in your community provides you with the power to help yourself—or local farmers—produce food to generate local wealth in an earth-bound carbon market. No economy, rich or poor, exists without food, because no economy, rich or poor, exists without soil.

The issues of peak oil, peak phosphorus, and other matters of assumed criticality are all indicators of our humble human need to replace one problem with another by addressing only the symptoms of our disease. In the same way that peak oil tells us that we have been too reliant on an unsustainable supply of oil, peak phosphorus tells us that we have relied for too long on industrial chemical farming. Soil and soil carbon can provide humanity the direct link to its very roots. It is part of our individual responsibility to ensure farmers have the right tools and the capacity to utilize their soil, based on their experiential management skills and those of past generations. In linking personal behavior with soil carbon, we weave the tapestry of soil quality into the reality of our daily existence.

To achieve this, we need to have a community understanding and response to the ability to grow our soils. The only place this can be achieved at scale is on the farm. Farms are the home and heart of our repeatable economic base. In a world carbon market, we have the first opportunity since the Industrial Revolution to once again include our environment in our economy. Every species lives within its economy, because to do otherwise is to perish. We can now join the evolution of economy by including the obvious in our accounts. Everything we now do and make can be predicated on its carbon value. You as an individual in this place are at an exciting starting point.

Alternate Collection Processes and Monetary Systems

In 1997, Richard Tong, a New Zealand–based environmental consultant, recycler, lecturer, and author, designed an innovative waste collection system called "Tag Bag." He wanted to break the domestic waste stream into a number of categories using existing collection systems, standard plastic shopping bags, and have the additional unique option of also collecting the plastic bags—thus keeping them out of the environment. The proposal would have used existing bins or bags—whichever suited the ongoing local government contract. The difficulty the proposal faced was that by the time it was being trialed by Zero Waste New Zealand and local waste reduction group, Waste

Not Auckland, the level of hysteria around plastic bags had grown to such an extent that the possibility of implementing such a scheme was already very low because of the "anti–plastic bag" movement. The concept would have enabled plastic bags and all forms of plastic to be kept out of the environment. It would have achieved a lot more than a simple container deposit system on a few bottles and cans. Opportunities are often missed by humanity because the fashionable view at the time obstructs an objective investigation of the usefulness of an idea or an object, and that view becomes such an obstruction that nothing the proponent can do will overcome it. As humans we can become so poisoned by concepts of the herd mentality that we fail to see or even consider a bigger picture. Mind you, even if it were successful in half of the countries around the world that utilize disposable plastic, a collection system will inevitably flounder if it fails to follow a natural circle of manufacture and return—of life and death.

There have been many recycling proposals that have died or were suffocated because the "herd mood" at the time—of the waste industry, community, or government—was not favorable. What we call the "waste stream" is a consequence of much of the environmental harm that society does to the planet. As is said elsewhere in this book, the molecular harm we do with our manufacturing processes creates waste in our rivers, land, and air—even prior to producing any product that goes to the market for a relatively short life. At the same time, the connections and understandings that could help repair this harm can in many ways be addressed by understanding and correcting our methods of managing of what we call waste.

In some areas, our level of understanding our environment seems so far off. We cannot seem to grasp the concept that we need a strong, vibrant, and healthy environment, replete with biodiversity, so as to mitigate the vast abuse we heap upon the earth as its human passengers. Many governments today are abandoning regulations in regard to environmental protection that had cost many lives and many years to put in place. They have made decisions that are focused on short-term financial gain at the expense of their very own children and the environment on which they will depend for survival. At the time of writing, the US government has just signed into law legislation to allow mining companies to dump wastes into river systems to save them clean-up costs—despite the fact that this will ultimately impact the water supplies of the very people the companies hope will buy their mined products.

State and federal governments in Australia are currently doing very little to control land clearing, which continues on a massive scale despite the fact that it has been conclusively proven that such behavior has only short-term gain. Ultimately the result can only be soil degradation, species extinction, and less rainfall. When seen in such a light, these behaviors are bloody-minded and fed by self-interest. It is mindboggling how, through irresponsible and short-sighted policies, people can bring despair, destruction, and extinction upon their own children This is especially so given that many concepts that have been put forward to better manage human behavior on our resource-limited planet are environmentally cheaper, less harmful, and relatively easy to introduce. I will suggest a few of these concepts here, hoping for more success than those who have tried earlier to make a change for the better.

Tag Bag

The Tag Bag idea, as already mentioned, was developed by Richard Tong of Auckland, New Zealand. Domestic waste is now collected in many countries by compactor trucks. The idea is of course to save travel, fuel, space, and time. In many parts of New Zealand, plastic collection bags were used rather than lidded bins or wheeled bins. The large plastic bags used for this purpose are purchased individually from local supermarkets. In 1997, when a trial was conducted on this proposal, this cost was $2 per bag. Each large bag contained on average nine smaller plastic shopping bags of various forms of rubbish. Collection of more materials as recyclables, paper, or organics would have meant both the purchase of additional bins or bags and additional collection vehicles. It is also worth keeping in mind that the original Tong design called for the breakdown of waste into many categories. The trial conducted by Waste Not Auckland was on four streams: organics, paper, recyclable and general waste.

A side-loader vehicle operation in Canberra in 1997, providing a single 240-liter bin to each of the 130,000 ground-level homes at $45 per bin, would have cost $5.5 million. Weekly collection of these same bins, at an average lift price of $1, was $130,000 per week, or $6.7 million per year. The preferred best-practice model at that time in adjoining New South Wales was a three-bin system. Each home had three bins, three collections per home, and separate vehicles for each collection (even if the same vehicle was used for the differing collections).

The concept with the Tag Bag trial was to separate waste into four specific categories in plastic shopping bags; but these smaller bags would have been put into, and collected in, a single bag or bin. The four bags were to be put into a cupboard or bin and progressively filled during the week. Once the week was over, the bags were to be sealed with a color-coded tag: green for organics, blue for paper, yellow for recyclables, and red for general waste. For the purposes of the trial, thirty households were given a double-sided A4 sheet of instructions and four rolls of green, blue, yellow, and red insulation tape. Participants were instructed to source-separate into the four categories and then tape the bag shut with the correct color tape. The trial ran for three months. We provided no assistance with kitchen tidies, hanging points, or additional information.

Success was measured by correct separation, and contamination never rose above 5 percent in any one bag. In practice, once fully implemented, the objective was to use a strip of ten single-color plastic tags, sold with every waste bag at the supermarket. A strip of ten, with a bag, would cost $10—approximately the cost of the existing bag. The intent was that the tags could be coded, and random inspection that revealed successful separation would have been rewarded with loyalty points or prizes. Given the success of the trial, it was estimated that the same program rolled out throughout Auckland City would have reduced domestic collected waste to landfill by around 80 percent. Sufficient funds could have been saved to have many thousands of dollars in value of prizes every month as encouragement and engagement. The bags would have gone to a location where they would have been electronically and automatically separated by the bar codes on the bags. The bags would be opened mechanically, with the contents sent over a checking line to detect and remove contamination.

The use of a single collection vehicle would dramatically lower cost. Because the bags could not be compacted there would have been more truck journeys, but the cost of infrastructure and transport could still have been dramatically reduced. Keep in mind that trucks would have had extended, higher sides to increase capacity. The use of the standard plastic bag as the source-separation system, controlled by the householder, meant that a large percentage of infrastructure costs would already have been met by the supermarket. By using the ubiquitous plastic bag, the system could easily have been biased to collect plastic bags and sheet plastics, which have become common in packaging and are now a worldwide environmental sea pollutant. As an additional benefit, by using prizes and encouragement, teamed with built-in biases, the vast majority of plastic bags would have been removed from the environment and could have been recycled back into more plastic bags or tags for the system.

The Tag Bag system also provided the following benefits:
- Entirely paid for by the users
- Reward- rather than guilt-driven
- Uses existing materials already in the system as infrastructure for collection
- Consistent size of container or bag
- Number of bags used can vary to suit the market or the household
- Can include commercial add-ons and reward points
- Prizes can "jackpot"
- Rewards could include lottery tickets and prizes
- Could apply pressure to change behavior and reduce specific consumption
- A price bias can be applied to different colors
- Can apply carbon credits or environmental rewards
- Delivers an 80 percent diversion

- Can be color-coded, electronically coded, bar-coded, or electronic chip–coded
- Can be varied to suit any size of population
- Can reduce rates and fees
- Single vehicle collection
- Single driver operation
- Supports all operational health & safety issues
- Suited to high-rise apartments, which could obtain the same outcome

Tag Bag demonstrated that people are willing to participate and cooperate in recycling programs. As was similarly indicated in the later City to Soil organics program, people are not, in fact, as silly as the industry and government would have us believe. Given a positive outcome, people will engage and participate if they have the right information, tools, and motivation.

The single biggest issue we faced when we proposed this system in New Zealand, and later in Australia, was the plastic bag itself. By the time we proposed the Tag Bag system to the New South Wales government, the standard one-use plastic shopping bag had been demonized by environmentalists, NGOs, and government agencies. As a last resort we tried submitting a proposal through a large commercial consultancy in Wollongong, to use their professional standing as consultant engineers and their links to government as a respected consultancy, but due to the political situation with plastic bags we did not even receive a hearing. The matter was rejected out of hand. The bag itself—the most important piece of infrastructure—which had no financial cost to the household, was the handicap.

When the proposal was previously put forward in New Zealand and Australia, the largest single impediment was the plastic bag itself. However, things have changed since the initial trial in New Zealand. The first and most important change is the compostable plastic bag for food collections. Another seems to be the shrinking size of the Radio Frequency Identification (RFID) chip that has been used to identify a specific bin location and that can also be used for other identification and location purposes. One RFID chip has reportedly been designed to be of edible size and included in food to provide information on nutrition. Householders may alternatively be able to purchase plastic clips to close the bag that include a chip.

The clips with RFID chips, bags with RFID chips, or bags with barcodes could be registered to the individual as they move through the checkout via their personal loyalty or credit card, with the details transferred to a personal account located on a common website. The website could provide information on food use and nutrition, growing food at home, seed suppliers, and compost supplies. In the current City to Soil program, the compostable bag has become traceable through use of a modified Tag Bag system in which the numbers stamped on individual bags can be allocated to the person's street address.

To gain full acceptance and to ensure flexibility, the system must work in high-rise, ground-level, and terraced housing. The system needs to allow the bag itself to carry the identification, which can be traced from the point of sale to the point of recovery. This could be achieved using the above model. The system could be focused as a commercial model in which the participant pays to join, is identified as owning a specific roll of bags, and could be rewarded with prizes when a bag selected at random is found to contain no contamination.

This concept suggests a real-life investment in change that is intended to address the specific issues related to recycling in densely populated cities, while at the same time addressing the broader re-cycling issues in a whole-of-community benefit context. In so doing, it recognizes that this program could be a first step in achieving sus-tainability in slum areas. The focus of this process is to maximize the self-sufficiency of the slum areas of cities in terms of materials use and re-use to create the maximum level of resource support that technolog-ical, financial, and human resources will permit. It is a practical process that would readily work in any large city that is drowning in plastic.

This proposal cites six immediate objectives that are required for beneficial outcomes:

- To assess and value the level of investment required to make the changes proposed and to access those financial resources from two distinct sources.

- To create extended producer responsibility of manufactured products, specifically plastic bags, and opportunity and other direct costs associated with government expenditure dealing with emergency and routine sanitation problems associated with wastes.
- To capture the value of materials passing through slum areas by collecting them carefully, in a way that keeps each material free from contamination so that it can easily and productively be reused.
- To create as local a reprocessing infrastructure as possible so that the production loops are as short as possible for each material.
- To ensure that all benefits from this development are retained as locally as possible and are spread as widely as equity permits.
- To account for all of this activity environmentally and socially, as well as financially, and introduce carbon accounting as a useful tool in support of this project.

Material Recycling in Densely Populated Areas

Most large, cosmopolitan cities have a broad mix of complex housing accommodation. Poorer areas and smaller businesses often struggle to recycle materials. Among their problems are the inability to apply infrastructure such as wheeled bins or boxes, which would normally be used with recycling programs in other regions, due to the limitations of space and the inability to get collection vehicles into the area to facilitate collections. The density and shapes of building structures and the lack of space to store or hold materials in urban areas also presents difficulties. Litter in inner-city areas is likewise difficult to control, and pollution and blocking of drains, streams, and rivers raises problems relating to both human health and broad social amenity. Of particular interest is the fact that flooding in central urban areas after severe storms is often caused by waste plastic materials, particularly grocery bags, which block drains and gutters. Plastic bags are estimated to have accounted for up to 40 percent of the damage caused by blocked drains when Typhoon Ondoy struck the Philippines in 2009. Plastic bag pollution within the city of Manila resulted in extensive damage and loss of life during the flooding events.

The principal complaint against the plastic shopping bag, apart from visual pollution, is that they are not collected in any great quantity, and as a result many millions of the bags find their way into the environment every year. Here they block drains, pollute waterways and oceans, and choke or cause starvation to a vast array of animals. The challenge of any proposal to utilize the bags for source separation and collection of materials is to find the correct level and mode of incentive to encourage the population to retain the bags, to fill them with the appropriate materials, and to get them to a point for collection. The objective is to achieve as close to 100 percent collection as possible while at the same time having local industry support the initiative and utilizing the collected bags in a remanufacturing program.

The issues facing councils in larger, diverse cities, in terms of poorer populations and their living conditions, are similar in some ways to how things were in the past in the city of Curitiba in Brazil.[22] In Curitiba, the inability to supply waste services to the large population living in the slum areas was resulting in increasingly poor health. While government did not encourage slum dwelling, it was obliged to provide health and medical facilities to the entire community. The cost of providing health services to slum dwellers was rising exponentially as population increased and living conditions deteriorated. Community health was badly affected by the dumping of a range of wastes within the housing area. This in turn encouraged vermin and other vectors and their associated diseases.

To reduce waste and its associated problems, Mayor Jaime Lerner encouraged people to bring their waste materials to a central location where they were provided food and transport vouchers. The net result was an efficient and effective waste collection process and dramatically improved community health, particularly among the poorer areas. The

---

22. "Jaime Lerner," Wikipedia, accessed 9 July, 2019,
    https://en.wikipedia.org/wiki/Jaime_Lerner/.

cost of providing food and transport vouchers was more than offset by the reduction in disease and ill-health among the slum dwellers. This or a similar model could be used in other cities, with a number of alterations and exceptions, to enable recycling and reuse of the vast majority of the material collected. There was a need in the Curitiba circumstance to look at the total budget associated with community health, transport, waste management, and social amenity. This required the imprimatur of the mayor, as he was the only person who could both view the total budget cost of these elements and drive the issue from a whole-of-community perspective. The application of this proposal within other cities will require the support and endorsement of the mayor and council if it is to succeed; otherwise, individual budgetary concerns would stifle the project.

As climate change develops, storm and tempest damage will increase, and insurance agencies will become more reluctant to provide services in places where loss is probable. Indeed, insurance agencies may well pursue their losses in the courts or simply fail to insure property owners where risk is inevitable. Some coastal home owners in parts of the world are already finding their properties "red-lined" as uninsurable due to the uncertainty of climate change. Rising insurance costs may inevitably be met by the local council, with negative impacts following on to the manufacturer of the goods producing the problem. It could readily be argued that, from a community perspective, the recycling of plastic bags makes sense both for the city, which pays the bulk of the costs for storm and tempest damage, and for the manufacturers of plastic products.

We all have a vested interest in seeing plastic bags removed from the streets of our cities. Local governments would benefit from reduced budgetary costs for sanitation and emergency relief, and manufacturers would gain from the consistent supply of manufacturing inputs at reduced costs from locally recycled plastic that are cheaper than imports.

The proposal needs to engage plastic bag manufacturers in the program as the end recyclers of the collected bags. Manufacturers would help invest in the system by agreeing to make three specific colored recycling bags for the program. They might want to contribute further as a collective or association if encouraged to think of taking their extended producer responsibilities seriously.

Elements of the system could include:

- Identification of the number of materials streams for collection—e.g., organics, all containers, paper/cardboard, and residuals
- A fully resourced education program for the entire community
- A method of payment for recycling; this will require careful thought, but it could include a mixture of cash-value food coupons, prizes, transport subsidies, and the like
- A full-cost evaluation of the last flood event, including health and community costs, so that the level of annual subsidy from this source can be determined
- Identification of potential savings and cost reallocation to the program from other areas
- Use of the City to Soil no-shred, no-odor, compost process and use of the compost outputs in the production of local food.

Benefits would include:

- A comprehensive recycling program for the entire city
- Engagement of available labor at the lowest socioeconomic level to implement the program
- Engagement of the community at all levels in the value of resources
- Massive reductions in community health costs
- Extensive reductions in vermin and other disease vectors in all housing areas
- An extensive and efficient waste collection service without the use of large vehicles
- Reductions in energy cost for the collection of waste
- Cleaner rivers, streams, and drains
- Reduced odor from storm water and river systems
- An extensive community employment program, delivering better community outcomes

- Comprehensive entry-level employment for those with poor literacy skills.

This system has the potential to deliver a multitude of community benefits in terms of waste management and community health, while at the same time developing a whole-of-city approach to recycling without incurring prohibitive infrastructure costs. Many thousands of plastic bags can be made from the plastic needed to make a single recycling bin or box. The added benefit of using the plastic bag is that with the appropriate washing, pelletizing, and remanufacturing equipment, the same materials could go around the city numerous times without having an adverse effect on either the bag manufacturer or the quality of bags produced, while boosting local employment and profits. Also, by providing an incentive for the collection of source-separated materials, the level of materials captured, in conjunction with the number of bags captured, should be extensive. The processing of these materials would then create vast employment potential in upstream materials recovery, baling, washing, reprocessing, remanufacturing, composting, and food production.

A Little More on Plastic Bags

One of the most difficult properties of plastic bags is their permanence. Even biodegradable bags only break down into smaller bits in the environment.

> To be harmless in the environment, plastic bags need to be either fully recovered or fully compostable.

In fact, if not exposed to ultraviolet sunlight, they verge on indestructible. If they are exposed to UV light, they become deadly, because they fragment into tiny pieces and are taken up by every living thing. Their indestructibility, however, is what makes them so useful in the first place. They could potentially be used to collect every other form of plastic, with little or no need for bins. You can fit twenty plastic bags in one pocket; they have little or no weight, and they can be manufactured in different colors.

While the removal of single-use plastic bags from supermarkets in developed countries may seem admirable, this action will likely only effect countries such as Norway, Australia, Switzerland, Denmark, the Netherlands, Germany, Ireland, the United States, Canada, New Zealand, Singapore, Hong Kong, Sweden, Wales, Scotland, and England. These countries, which in one form or another utilize variations on English law, make up only around 10 percent of the world population. Plastic bags in less developed countries are used for everything from drink bottles to toilets, and a myriad of applications in between. They could also be used for aggregating materials, such as plastic, glass, and metal.

In many of these countries, plastic bags, as described in the earlier example, could take on a practical application in which they are used as almost the total infrastructure needed to recover every piece of organic waste, glass, metal, paper, and cardboard. Poorer communities often do not have garbage bins, despite the efforts of large waste companies. The benefit of having tools such as plastic bags in the hands of the poor is that they could also be paid to collect all manner of things as source-separated material, thus improving community diets and health, reducing litter, stopping flooding, and reducing waste management costs.

When the previously mentioned Tag Bag system was proposed, in some areas the reaction was blatant rejection. People would not even consider the proposal, even when it was demonstrated that such a system would have dramatically increased recycling and reduced domestic waste to landfill by up to 80 percent. The great advantage of the system was the ability to build into the process a price or benefit bias to a particular materials stream. This meant that source-separation could have been guaranteed, with no need to change collections infrastructure and with massive cost reduction in the type of trucks used for collection.

There are contra arguments, of course. Many of these highlight the need for action but do little or nothing in the longer term. In Asia there are accumulated piles of plastic that continue to grow simply because they are not moving back into production. How can it be that the Zabbaleen, who live in and around the slums of Cairo, can have a full plastic recovery and reprocessing plant underneath their home, but that this can't be achieved elsewhere? Does it mean that we need different processes in different countries? Or does it simply mean, once again, that we have failed in our model of being natural animals in a natural world? Vast quantities of plastic could be returned to production if the economic or social emphasis were placed on materials recovery. Yet many of us do little other than complain. It should also be remembered that anything that can be made from hydrocarbons can be made from carbohydrates.

Island

No single tree was left or saved
To build a small canoe
No boat nor craft
Nor wood for raft
To sail a sea so blue

No bird could sing upon a branch
For there was none to grasp
Was all cut down
For trees are round
And all for rollers cast

And as the wind-chilled headstones
Stood facing down the sea
No cloud could settle
To drop rain
So rain could never be

And so it died alone at sea
A land of stone
In all bird-free
A cut-out of humanity
A prehistory of you and me

CHAPTER 4
Source Separation

The collection of paper fiber, as mentioned in the introduction, was most likely one of our earliest human examples of understanding source separation of materials for recycling. Clean fiber is valuable fiber—it takes less work to process and produces a better-quality end product. This is still true in paper markets today.

A separate stream of any sort of material will have a better value at market. This basic principle is why collecting mixed materials as quickly as possible in compactor vehicles, with little or no thought to quality or cleanliness, simply does not make sense if you are attempting to get the best possible price from the market.

The waste industry and local governments have never really understood recycling collections. I recall visiting councils in Australia to promote recycling in the early 1980s, and council health and building inspectors, who in some bizarre way were generally responsible for waste, simply did not get it. In fact, they saw this newfangled idea of recycling as an unwelcome addition to a heavy workload. After World War II they had started using the US military engineers' concept of covered landfills instead of the usual hole at the edge of a creek or a beach, and anything other than burial was simply a distraction. As a result, any community recycling program, either through a service club or a community group, was generally independent of waste collections and was focused on cleanliness and quality. It was when councils were forced to take responsibility for recycling that the difficulties for source separation of materials really began. Once recycling collections became the subject of tendering processes, the battle to maintain quality really began.

From my recollections of the 1970s, recycling was originally a fundraiser for enthusiastic community groups, service clubs, scouts, and hospital auxiliaries. At that time, income was mainly focused on paper and cardboard. Later it moved to cans, as aluminum pushed steel out of the beer market. Around that same time, recycling became more structured and more broadly based, with the introduction of the blue box recycling system in Canada. The first full-scale, community-wide program based on the blue box was implemented in 1983. Prior to this, in 1977, Canadians Jack McGinnis and Derek Stephenson had formed Resource Integration Systems (RIS) to advise governments on successful recycling programs. There were, of course others around the world prior to this that can be pursued through other historically focussed documents.

During the late eighties and nineties the blue box system dominated the recycling service operations of various agencies worldwide. Placing recyclable material into a box was considered easy and convenient by householders.

It is clear, however, that as packaging expanded, and as recycling began to claim a larger part of the materials stream, that recyclers had moved into an area the waste industry saw as its own.

This has resulted in many recycling contracts around the world being handed to waste companies by the aforementioned local governments. The process was seen to be nothing more than a variation on the collection of waste with the same vehicles. It is clear from the successes in Wales that the process is far more than this.

The waste industry and local governments have often been resistant to changes that could improve product quality in recycling. The result of this poor decision making has resulted in China's refusal to take compacted recycled products mixed as waste. The indisputable response to China's position is for all collectors of material to improve quality via source separation. As mentioned earlier, this is precisely what the people of Wales have done to become one of the best recycling countries in the world. The essence of the success of recycling in Wales is a source-separation model called Cleanstream, which was developed and refined by the community group Cylch. Designed in 2000 by Cylch's former chairman, the late Mike Croxford, MBE, and its CEO, Mal Williams, Cleanstream became the "Collections Blueprint." Materials are collected from the home, sorted at the curbside, and then loaded onto the truck in segmented compartments. Any mistakes made by the householder are left in the crate. This has resulted in a contamination rate of less than 0.05 percent, and any non-recyclables are left to be placed in the waste bin.

Recycling improved in Europe after the EU passed the Landfill Directive in 1999.[23] The law raised awareness of the fact that in a world of limited resources, we can't afford to bury or burn anything lest we, like many of our fellow travelers on this planet, too became extinct.

With statutory weight-based targets set for waste reduction and diversion from landfill, two lines of thought emerged to address the issue in Europe. The first was to continue business as usual and simply use a modified process, with the same equipment for recycling as for waste. This meant collecting mixed recyclables and then taking them to an MRF for sorting. This of course results in high rejection rates and poor-quality materials due to contamination. The other option was to use a recycling system specifically designed to produce clean, uncontaminated materials for sale to the reprocessing industry. It called for materials to be kept separate from the very beginning—no mixing. Material streams were simply sorted at the curbside as they were loaded onto the truck.

For a long time, the waste industry method was able to prevail because reject rates could be disguised and because it was able to claim high recycling numbers under the protection of under-resourced regulators. Illegal exporting of waste materials took place and shipments were disguised as recycled materials because the exporting of waste is forbidden by law.

---

23. "The Landfill Directive Fact File," Rubbish Prohibited website, published 25 October, 2014, https://landfill-site.com/landfill-directive-fact-file.html/.

In the beginning, China and other Asian countries welcomed these shipments because their economies were growing rapidly, and materials were scarce. But as the situation in the Far East matured, these nations became much fussier about what they would accept. The doors finally closed in December 2017, when the Chinese announced what is known as the Chinese Sword: a ban on importing anything with a contamination rate by weight of more than 0.3 percent (later modified by negotiation to 0.5 percent), which no MRF could achieve.

Mixed material can no longer be disguised as recyclables for export to Asia. Unfortunately, waste companies, lumbered with low-quality materials that they cannot export, have been turning to incineration as an alternative destination for residual wastes. Some have also been pelletizing rejected materials to manufacture Refuse-Derived Fuel (RDF) for export to burn in under-utilized incinerators elsewhere. The Chinese rejection makes incineration look more economically attractive to those who have invested in the wrong collection methodology.

Fortunately—in Europe, at least—this sleight of hand has been spotted, and the EU has withdrawn funds for encouraging incineration, giving the clear message that the future does not lie in that direction. Allowing incineration would negate all of the EU's aspirations to create an efficient circular economy (i.e., zero waste).

So curbside-sorted collections are finally gaining ground as the only logical way to achieve quality products. It is a testimony to the power of the waste industry that this logical, simple method of recovering clean materials for repeated re-use could have been delayed so long.

Such is the power of vested interests.

What was sad about this determined resistance to change was that it prevented the establishment of local remanufacturing. It also made recycling look difficult and expensive. Worse still, it made recycling look like a huge problem and perpetuated the myth that the materials markets were fickle and weak. It made investment in recycling seem like a high-risk decision, when nothing could be further from the truth. Yes, change requires substantial investment to provide infrastructure for a new system and to educate the community in how to use it. But survey after survey revealed, "Give us the equipment to use and a reliable, easily understandable service and we'll use it." Few local authorities ever listened to that information. Those that did were ignored for a long time, even though they were highly successful.

Where recycling collections use the community engagement and curbside-sort method, there is little or no added cost for the collection. The system uses more collection trucks, but it does not require MRFs or Mixed Biological Treatment (MBT) plants, let alone incinerators of any sort. The revenues gained by selling the materials, and the avoidance of landfill and incineration costs, make it the cheapest system to use by far. Furthermore, and crucially, the method delivers the highest quality materials to market, assuring the highest revenues available.

What is often forgotten is that the previous old waste-collection-and-disposal system was generally 100 percent subsidized by public funds.

So, if source separation creates new opportunities. What are they?

Linking Resource Reuse and Recycling to Community Benefit

A great argument has erupted in the waste industry due to the Chinese refusing to allow waste into their country disguised as "recycled products." China will review the importation of all such materials in future years. In the longer term, this means that we must find valid uses for such products or stop manufacturing them.

Anyone who has visited China in the past twenty years has seen how difficult it has become for the Chinese to maintain air quality. As the West has placed increasing demand on China for the production of goods, and as the Chinese have willingly agreed to be the manufacturing base for a large percentage of the world's goods, the air quality has spiraled downward, to the point where it has been difficult in some areas to see more than several hundred meters. The air is thick with toxic fumes from industry and the production of energy.

It should have been obvious to anyone in the West that the delusion of continuing markets for recycled materials could not go on. The Chinese have simply drawn a line in the sand in regard to environmental protection that we all should take note of. One reason Chinese goods are so cheap, leaving aside potential slave labor and the willingness of the West to join in the abuse of the poor and disadvantaged, is the externalized cost of production—the smoke, dust, particulates, toxic gas, and poisonous water that have been dumped into Chinese communities and China's neighboring countries. These costs are not counted in the bill when you buy your new car, refrigerator, electric drill, or furniture. China will continue to apply more severe restrictions on environmental harm as demand for its goods increases and as its population grows. As stated elsewhere, every shirt, every shoe, every phone, every toaster has to be made by a human—up to 70 percent of the materials used in industry come from agriculture—as does the food that feeds the person who makes the goods. All of it comes from the farmer's soil. Every product imported from China represents part of its nation's soil.

However, the Chinese Sword highlights an opportunity for every community around the world to deal with its own recyclables.

The alternative to dumping waste into China, or some other part of Asia, is to develop local industry that can use our outputs in our own community.

Now I agree that this may not be practical in some situations, but keep in mind that it is not always necessary to spend millions to produce local products. Some recycling is very simple and requires no machinery or buildings at all. However, there is one very important element that should not be overlooked: the cause of the rejection of the products dumped into China is the lack of source separation! Recycled materials should not be mixed in the first place.

Keeping materials separate adds enormously to their value and usefulness. To be clear, when buyers in the various materials industries say they want to pay only for clean materials, they mean that they want materials that are uncontaminated by the presence of any other material. For example, glass is a prime contaminant of paper, and ceramics are a contaminant of glass.

An excellent example of a business that has benefited from source separation is Xtreme Waste in Raglan, New Zealand. Household dry recyclables and organic wastes are collected by a curbside-sorted operation, and all of the other materials that are not used in the homes of the local community are brought to a single transfer station where they are put into categories and either resold or recycled. In 2019, Xtreme Zero Waste turned over NZ$1.5 million and employed twenty-three full-time employees in sustainable jobs, in a community with a population a little over 3,000. The unique quality of Xtreme Zero Waste Raglan is that the community operation was developed without the support of the local council. They simply put themselves between the community and the landfill, extracted just about everything, and sold it back into the community to sustain their business. They are now a working model for the rest of New Zealand. This model can be made to work at any scale but is much easier with community and local council support.

The Social Enterprise model is also particularly useful as a vehicle to gain community support for the operation. It states loud and clear that you are in business to provide community and environmental benefit, not just to make profits for disinterested investors mostly living elsewhere.

What You Can Do in Your Community

Over the following pages I will provide examples of what you can do both at home and on a larger community scale to use your products in a beneficial way. All of it is predicated on the process of source separation.

Cleanliness and quality will always lead to better prices, better outputs, more employment, and more community income. Every community around the world is different in terms of permissible uses and regulations, manufacturing consents, and compliance—so be sure that what you plan to do is within the local law. The quantity of different materials will vary in different countries, and the ways in which you can deal with them may not be the same in all cases. However, you will find that there are many great recycling practices around the world. Some of the better models are those that are more defined, like Urban Ore in Berkeley, California, which operates its recycling program with twelve master categories (waste streams).[24]

I will outline a number of reuse and recycling options for different classes of materials. I first nominate a use and then identify the types of tools and machinery required to establish a business based on that use within your community. The step beyond this initial identification is to nominate quantities and the number of employees involved. There are numerous pieces of machinery, hand tools, and protective equipment required to run any of the listed operations. All relevant information about the process or services could be placed on a website to facilitate sales and an income stream. Access to other recycling information could be provided on the same basis. Also keep in mind that one material stream could be mixed with another material stream to make a totally different product.

The following list is in no way exhaustive; it is merely indicative. There are some very clever people out there who have found far better uses for materials than those originally intended. Having said that, new sources, uses, machinery, and processes develop almost every week, so you need to identify what you think will make money for you or for your community. Once you have done that, start chasing a value-adding proposition—you might be very pleasantly surprised!

---

24. Urban Ore website, http://urbanore.com/.

1. PAPER AND CARDBOARD

Paper products, as one stream, can make up to about 25 percent of total waste materials. Cardboard is simply the heavy-duty version of paper and can be used in much the same way as paper. It is made up of fiber and is mostly sourced from wood. Recycling has always been seen as the best option for paper, yet paper has numerous uses. Also, the difficulty for many communities is that the nature of paper itself may dictate whether it is better to use it locally or to recycle it back into paper.

Take for example the situation in remote locations in Australia, such as Condobolin, where the town is many hours from a main population center. Even if its paper and cardboard were in fact recycled, it would do more environmental harm than good to ship it to markets. Also, in such a situation, paper and cardboard can play a far better role for the community as soil organic matter. They are carbon, after all.

Almost everything transported to remote areas comes boxed in cardboard. Condobolin has a sewage system, so it also has a source of biosolids. If all the town's paper and cardboard were soaked in a tank until the fibers started to separate, it could then be mixed with biosolids and green waste to make a high-quality compost that could be sold to households and farmers to improve soil organic matter, reduce fertilizer use, and save on landfill. The unused space in landfill becomes more valuable every year, even in remote locations, so it may even be viable to simply make the product and give it away. Paper that has been contaminated by food can also be used in composting.

Alternatively, paper makes excellent animal bedding. Or, when mixed with chicken, horse, or pig manure, or sewage sludge, it can make a good compost or food for earthworms, which process it into fertilizer.

Paper fiber has a number of other uses as well that we shall investigate. Keep in mind that options for material reuse depend as much on the imagination of the user and the nature of the product as on anything else. When paper is recycled, its fibers progressively get shorter, so you need to keep adding new fiber to make the product fully functional. Paper makers use a range of other products as fiber sources, including flax, hemp, cotton clothing, and various types of weeds.

Also keep in mind that your community may want to first seek a high-value option for any given material stream, retaining composting as a large-scale backup. Be sure to check with your local council in regard to relevant regulations.

Here some reuse options for paper:

- **Small scale manufacturing into hand-made paper**
  Craft paper has relatively high value. Consider a printing operation or an artisan training programs to make specialty cards.
- **Shred for use as packaging**
  Paper and cardboard make great box stuffing when shredded. It can be used to transport glass, ceramics, and other fragile materials. There is a commercial cardboard box shredder that provides a half-cut to the length of the cardboard, allowing it to be wrapped around breakables. I recommend marketing this material secondarily for compost, animal bedding, or garden mulch.
- **Shred and use as housing insulation (mixed with a fire retardant)**
  Check local regulations in regard to this—if used in a commercial operation it may require a large and continual supply; you don't want to run out if your business depends on it.
- **Pulp paper to make into planter pots, egg cartons, etc.**
  Again, this requires a continual supply if you plan to scale your business. That said, you can make hanging-basket planter pots from shredded paper and cardboard as a school arts project.
- **Mixed paper and straw for acoustic insulation panels**
  Be sure to fireproof your product and ensure that it complies with local regulations; a continual supply is also important.
- **Shredded for use as animal bedding**
  Shredded paper and cardboard are excellent under chickens, pigs, and other animals. Once covered with manure and urine it can be used as garden mulch or in compost. If it has sufficient nutrients and is wet and under cover, it can be readily processed by earthworms.
- **Pulp/shred and mix with old sewage sludge for worm food, or compost it with yard waste**

Shredded paper and cardboard make an excellent carbon input for worm composting. Don't be concerned about ink; most printers these days use vegetable inks.

- **Shred, mix with grass seed / vermicastings, and apply as mulch**
  If you use this method, you will need to find some means to hold the product together, such as tar. Unshredded paper can also be used under general mulch as the base of a no-till or "lasagna" garden. The paper serves as a weed barrier and will eventually break down to form soil.
- **Shred and mix with food and yard waste to produce compost**
  Paper or cardboard are just another carbon source. Blend it with the proper amount of nitrogen to make a quality compost.
- **Sell to recycling markets**
  This is perhaps a little obvious—but this use is low on the list of possibilities.
- **Biochar—generate power then activate the residual for use in soils**
  You will need continual quantities for this process—or simply make it part of a fuel source. When correctly managed, using a high-quality down-draft gasifier, you can get both energy from wood gas and biochar for soil improvement, without releasing gas into the atmosphere.

Processes and types of equipment

- **Shredding: paper shredder or hammermill, hand tools, and gloves**
  There are many different paper shredders, from the simple few sheets–type up to industrial models. The small one is relatively cheap and will work fine for households that are recycling small quantities of paper. A hammermill is an excellent tool to make a light, fluffy product from cardboard or paper. If you use the type that connects to a power take-off on a farm tractor, be sure to take out the grate on the hammermill. It will make a wonderful product for worm farming or bedding.

- **Composting: front end loader, mulcher, hand tools, and gloves**
  There are many ways to make compost at scale. Some methods do not require turning, but these may need a covering, inoculation, and a way to keep it wet. No matter what process you use, you will need a front-end loader to handle your material, to turn it, and to load it onto vehicles.
- **Vermiculture: worms, shovels, front end loader** *(at scale)*, **hand tools, and gloves**
  Shredded paper or paper pulp—made by soaking paper or cardboard in water for about a week—is perfect for worm farming. Vermiculture can be done at any scale, from a small container to a football field. It produces a high-quality, water-soluble product that can be used as a biostimulant foliar fertilizer or as a soil drench.
- **Pots or egg cartons: hydro-pulper, moulding machine, hand tools, and gloves**
  This requires machinery to suit the scale; all are readily available.
- **Bales for transport: baling machine, compactor, hand tools, and gloves**
  The size of your baler will depend on the end market, your mode of transport, and the quantity you are baling. Most organizations who will take your paper and cardboard will help with the appropriate machinery because it will save them money and will provide better bulked product with fewer handling costs.

2. FOOD AND KITCHEN SCRAPS

Food scraps, along with other organic materials, are usually buried in landfills in order to prevent health problems. If we can keep food out of our bins, we will have removed one of the main reasons for landfills. This would also allow us to return an incredibly valuable product to our soils. Food scraps are high in minerals and nutrients; these can be returned to the soil through composting and worm farming. You can also turn your food waste into a hydrolysate by macerating it and mixing it with carbohydrates and an inoculant.

Both communities and individual householders can be taught to compost. Composting can help families save money and eat better at the same time. Most people don't know how to manage a compost heap, though. A compost heap with food in it can be an uncontrolled landfill that attracts vermin. A closed worm bin is the safest way to process food into a high-quality form of compost. Larger scale operations can be developed to redirect the composted products to agriculture. You can also use the Quick Return Method, an enclosed process developed before World War II by Maye Bruce.[25] No matter what scale or method you use, always remember to check with regulators.

Processing methods for food scraps:

- **Bury it**
  The simplest way to use food scraps is to bury them in your garden with something heavy on top for several weeks. You will find that worms love it, and your soil will improve dramatically. You need a stainless-steel, lidded container in the kitchen, which is easy to clean, and several bricks to place on top of the spot where you bury your food waste to prevent animals from digging it up. This, of course, depends on where you live. You may get the odd potato or tomato plant you don't want, but these are easily removed.

- **Compost or worm farming**
  You can devise a program to teach individuals how to compost and garden. This will improve community health and will reduce disposal to landfill at the same time.

- **Commercial composting**
  This requires source separation of materials at the household. I always recommend the City to Soil process, which utilizes an odor-free bin for food scraps in the kitchen. Smells caused by the commercial composting of food scraps are no longer a problem. Technology is available to overcome this, all of which is open source, protected by Community Commons, and free.[26]

---

25. Maye E. Bruce, "Common-Sense Compost Making," Journey to Forever website, accessed 9 July, 2019, http://journeytoforever.org/farm_library/QR/QRToC.html/.
26. Gerrygillespie.net

- Protein hydrolysate
  This process can be done at any scale. You will need to make and use an inoculant product based on lactobacillus that is described on my website, gerrygillespie.net. The food waste is macerated with water, carbohydrate is added as an energy source, and then inoculant is added. This produces a foliar fertilizer that can be used on gardens and crops.

Tools needed:
- Food burial
  A stainless-steel bucket in the kitchen, a small shovel, and gloves.
- Home composting or vermicomposting
  A small shredder—look for one that is slow and quiet. You can get hammer mill–type machines that spin very quickly and shred well, but the slower ones are safer. You will also need a rake, pruning shears, gloves, and safety goggles.
- Commercial composting
  Larger shredders, front end loaders, and safety gear.
- Protein hydrolysate
  Containers in which to make the product, a macerator to suit the scale of your process, one-way fermentation locks, and storage containers.

3. TIMBER

Timber can range from old furniture and pallets to building materials such as wall framing and support beams. Much of the timber from building sites should arrive at your processing site in separate loads or with little contamination. You can encourage builders to source separate by charging less than the local landfill. If builders supply directly to you for resale, ask them to take a little more care when demolishing so as to minimize damage. Keep a close eye out for materials that are contaminated with poisons or preservatives and be sure they don't get into your compost process.

Products and processing methods for timber:

- **Resale**
  You can readily salvage and sell products like furniture, pallets, and timber. Try to provide a free collection service if possible—once you are out there collecting you will be offered all sorts of new opportunities.

- **Repair or clean-up for sale**
  Start a fix-it shop where people can use shared tools and receive instruction to do their own repairs or to recondition items. Reclaim parts and sell them for reconstruction of larger items. You can also repair items as they come in for direct resale. You can often find a retired joiner or upholsterer who is prepared to help others learn some aspect of their trade.

- **Mulch or shred for compost or landscaping**
  Anything that is not contaminated can be composted once shredded down to a suitable size. You can either sell it as a mulch or compost it with other organic wastes such as food, yard trimmings, or paper.

- **Firewood**
  There is always a need for barbeque wood or kindling; this can be bagged or bundled for sale.

- **Animal Bedding**
  Grind the timber for poultry and animal bedding—then reuse it as compost once dirty.

The tools you need are:

- **A full range of hand tools**
  Everything from chisels to hammers, crowbars, and screwdrivers, plus a good selection of power tools, drills, saws, etc.

- **Manual and/or mechanical log splitter**
  This will be invaluable in the longer term, so get the biggest one you can afford. While cheaper options might be available, they will also limit your capability in the future.

- **Grinder or shredder**
  Anything you can't sell as timber you can sell or use as mulch or compost. Once again, if you do need one, buy the biggest you can afford.
- **Front-end loader**
  If your operation is big enough to warrant a front-end loader, also investigate what attachments are compatible with the tractor's power take-off. Numerous saws, log splitters, hammermills, and other attachments are available and may save you more investment in the longer term.

4. PLASTIC

Plastic makes up an increasingly large percentage of the total material sent to landfills. One difficulty with plastic is that there are so many varieties of the polymer from which it is made. Companies often use combinations of polymers, rendering the final product non-recyclable because the mix they use may not include enough of a particular material to make reprocessing economically viable. Packaging does keep food fresh, and in that sense prevents waste, but do we need packaging made from non-renewable resources or from renewable ones?

Several types of plastic have reliable markets. You can work to sustain those markets by encouraging manufacturers to use plastic polymers that can readily be resold. Producers may have accords and working programs with governments to reduce landfill, but little has been done to change current practices.

It is possible to build your own small-scale community plastics reprocessing plant. An organization in the Netherlands called Precious Plastics markets a small-scale plastics manufacturing plant that can take collected plastics from the cleaning stage to completed products.[27]

---

27. Precious Plastics website, https://preciousplastic.com/.

Plastic is choking our oceans and, despite claims to the contrary, container deposits in a small number of countries around the world, while helpful in a small way, will do little to actually reduce the materials that are progressively destroying our fisheries and wildlife. Container deposits are focused on litter programs, and as such they address little more than 1 percent of the total material stream we call waste. The countries in which these programs are legally controllable contain only 10 percent of the world's population. If we are going to stop the damage caused by plastics, we are going to have to put pressure on manufactures to do a lot more to prevent their products getting into our waterways and causing environmental harm. This requires communities to take a far more strategic position on their short- and long-term use of fossil oil products to make fuels and plastics. To achieve longer term goals, we need to:

- Apply pressure to governments to cease the wanton extraction of fossil oils and to encourage research into alternatives
- Through community groups, apply pressure to manufacturers to reduce packaging
- Encourage packaging producers to use easily recycled resins for which there are markets, such as PET and HDPE, and to guarantee take-back
- Encourage producers to use single types of materials in packaging and to eliminate overwraps and double-packing
- Encourage manufacturers to reduce or avoid additives, mixtures, pigments, and multi-layers of different resins that cannot be recycled
- Encourage your community to buy reusable packaging, as well as foods packed in glass, metal, and cardboard
- Encourage alternatives to plastic shrink wrap and plastic straws
- Encourage the use of reusable bags for shopping.

Plastic is made from hydrocarbon, a non-renewable resource. There should be, and are, far more significant benefits your community can get from this material. In the future, plastic will be made from carbohydrates rather than hydrocarbons—several manufacturers, including BASF and Nova Mont, already make fully compostable plastic products. These are not just biodegradable. Biodegradable products merely disintegrate into small particles and remain in the environment; they don't compost. Until the day comes when all plastics are fully compostable, insured against loss into the environment, or guaranteed to be recycled, here are some good reuses for plastic:

- **Turn all your shredded plastics into concrete building bricks for local community projects**
  The New Zealand company Enviroplaz started creating plastic bricks using a mixture of polymers and concrete in 1996. It has moved into a range of other products in recent years, all based on recycling plastic and glass.[28]
- **Shred and store for future use above or below ground**
  (it's only going to get more valuable)
  If you are going to attempt this you may need licenses, consents or permits, so check with local authorities.
- **Support the establishment of a local plastic injection molding business**
  In some remote corners of the world there are plastic injection businesses using old injection molding machines that make things like protection caps for steel posts, support frames for reinforcing in concrete slabs, or plastic frames for car license plates.
- **Arrange to market your product under specific conditions; sort and bale for resale into overseas markets**
  While countries like China are refusing to take mixed plastic products containing contamination, there are opportunities still available to sell into other world markets—but it must be clean to get a decent price. Source separation is imperative.

Processing and handling equipment:
- Recovery sorting line
  A sort line will enable you to remove contamination from mixed

---

28. Enviroplaz website, https://enviroplaz.com/.

plastics. If materials are source separated in the first place you shouldn't need this—but a sort line can be handy for a number of reasons.

- **Shredding equipment**
  If you are considering injection molding you will need some form of shredding equipment. Injection molding can be used to generate bulk transportable molded pieces like supports and picket caps.
- **Granulating equipment**
  This is important if you are going into the broader market to sell your product.
- **Baling equipment**
  This is important if you are going to sell in bulk without any pre-processing.
- **Forklift**
  Everything you will be moving will be big and bulky— this is imperative.

5. TEXTILES AND CLOTHING

Materials made from cotton, silk, and wool have a range of reuses, from resale to composting. There are many needs in your community or someone else's for quality, functional clothing. The key to preventing waste here is to reduce consumption, avoiding "fast fashion" and its emphasis on minimal use and rapid replacement. Focus on textiles and clothing made of natural, rather than synthetic, fabrics. And bear in mind the hidden environmental and social costs that prop up the production of cheap garments.

Processing methods for textiles and clothing:

- **Sell or donate your used clothes for reuse**
  Use drop-off facilities or arrange pick up services.
- **Recycle and redesign clothes**
  Many new businesses have begun on the basis of redesigning clothing and selling it in-store or on-line.

- **Use as rags**
  The demand for quality rags in the mechanical and motor vehicle repair industry is high—the potential exists to provide an ongoing service by washing these rags and returning them to the same businesses.
- **Shred and mix with other fiber for papermaking**
  You can produce a range of unique business cards and stationery using blue jeans and other quality clothing made from natural fibers.
- **Shred and compost with high-nitrogen materials**
  This isn't the best use of old clothing, but it can save landfill. Used clothing also makes excellent covers for worm bins and compost heaps.
- **Bale and ship for reprocessing elsewhere**
  You will need someone who knows their fibers, but this can be a viable and profitable business.

Processing equipment:

- **Manual sorting tables**
  A very large wooden or metal surface is required for sorting and sacking; you will have to build your own to get a suitable size.
- **All-weather protection**
  Find decent shed space with climate control—people will be standing still for long periods in all weather.
- **Equipment for baling and boxing**
  A standard wool baler or something similar should be fine.
- **Safety gear**
  Supply gloves and light goggles; a quality vacuum extraction fan is needed to manage dust.

6. METALS

There are two broad types of metals: ferrous and nonferrous. Chances are there is already a nonferrous metals collector in your area. Nonferrous metals include aluminum, brass, and copper. They are all very valuable. If there is no collector in your area, your organization or business has a good opportunity to add some value to your operation. Selling of both ferrous and non-ferrous metals can be arranged through dealers in larger towns. Check out the prices thoroughly before entering into any agreements.

Ferrous metals can be found almost anywhere. Many farming properties over the years have accumulated large stockpiles of old cars and machinery just waiting for collection. Ferrous metal is not worth a lot per ton, but as with most other products, a large pile of it is definitely worth something. Stockpile if you can and sell when you get the price you want.

Resale and processing methods:

- If you are collecting metal for resale in a country area, find someone locally who has a general knowledge of equipment. Older equipment can be very valuable, more for its historical or antique value than because it is functional or contains raw metal. Don't dismantle anything you suspect is whole or vintage until you have a second opinion on it!
- If you can, try to arrange a special day for the collection of metals. Do this in association with community services groups such as Lions, Cubs, Scouts, Rotary, etc. You can use service clubs to line up a series of collection points. The job will be a lot easier if you are collecting from drop-off points than from all over the countryside.

Here are a few methods for handling metals:

- **Repair for reuse or sale** *(does it have historical value?)*
  You will need someone who knows machinery generally—a mechanic might be the preference. A generalist is better than a specialist.
- **Items such as angle, bar, plate, or pipe can be used as a resource base for a small blacksmithing or welding business**
  Blacksmithing is an old but valuable skill. You can either create a specialist manufacturing business or specialize in repairs and maintenance.

- Sort out mixed scrap metal, dismantle and clean it to identify reusable material, remove contaminants, and upgrade for recycling industry use
  This is a very worthwhile phase. Sorting for value before sale is important—in many instances it can dramatically improve the value of the material.
- Sort into ferrous and nonferrous
  This is basic but very important—otherwise your buyer could take serious advantage of you.
- Use machinery to strip coatings off of wire (do not do this by burning—it generates high levels of dioxin and is very toxic)
  Good, cheap machinery is available through the internet.
- Recover rare metals such as mercury (in switches and electrical products) and gold (in computer scrap)
  Talk to specialist buyers in regard to this type of process—you may want to pass on bulk rather than fighting through the details.

For processing equipment, you will need:

- Hand tools
  Look for a large collection of second-hand mechanic's tools plus all the usual electric- and battery-powered hand tools. You will need every one of them eventually.
- Welder and oxyacetylene
  These skills and tools are very important for repair, maintenance, and general building.
- Metal shredders and cutters
  Whether you will need these depends on how much recycling you are doing, as opposed to manufacturing; but you will still need hand tools.
- Industrial baler for aluminium scrap and steel cans
  You will need to have the right sort of equipment to ensure good compaction pressure.
- Forklift
  Everything you will be moving will be big and bulky.

- Safety gear
  Safety googles suitable for welding, gloves of all weights,
  full-face masks, heavy-duty clothing, steel-capped boots,
  and ear muffs.

7. PLANT DEBRIS AND OFFCUTS

Plant offcuts, prunings, and clippings are some of the most easily
processed materials. If you make compost and have access to plant
offcuts, all you need are used plastic pots to create a nursery operation.
The main income from the operation might be the sale of compost.
However, fresh cuttings and plants that have been left for composting
can be potted up for resale. It is a very simple process—a few seconds
of your time and a bit of your compost can easily result in a valuable
sale. Keep in mind environmental regulations in regard to processing
and transportation of organic waste—these materials can cause severe
contamination and destruction of wildland areas, so take care to comply with the law.

Processing methods for plant debris and offcuts:

- **Re-pot live plants and sell them**
  It only takes a pot and a bit of dirt to produce a
  saleable commodity.
- **Compost with other high nitrogenous materials**
  This is another compost input that will boost the quality
  of what you already have.
- **Use composted product as feedstock for a worm farm**
  You can add considerable value to compost by putting earthworms through it. The quality of the product will allow you
  to sell it by the liter rather than by the ton.
- **Shred and compost in windrows**
  For a higher-quality product, use the covered compost process
  described on my website; you don't lose as much of the bulk of
  your material, and it should have a much higher level of humus
  when complete.

You will need:

- **Sorting and potting table**
  Give yourself lots of workable area, with storage underneath.
- **Hand tools**
  Small and large shovels—hand-, post-, and square-mouthed—all will be needed.
- **Simple hothouse structure for all-weather protection of plants**
  A treasure on a freezing night to protect your investments.
- **A selection of plastic pots from domestic discards**
  You will find these in thrift stores, garden clubs, and suppliers—perhaps ask for them to be put away for you or provide a drop-off bin.
- **Shredder**
  Size here depends on what you are doing—if you are only working with soft plant material, a small, slow, noiseless shredder rather than a hammermill may suffice.
- **Safety equipment**
  Gloves of all types, goggles, ear muffs, full-face mask, etc.
- **Front end loader**
  Again, if composting on a large scale, everything you will be moving will be big and bulky, so this is important.

8. GLASS

The market for glass has always been limited. If you are not selling it back to the manufacturer, you must find an alternate use. This field has some unusual options. Glass can be used in sandblasting, or it can also be used as a color-separated or comingled material for the manufacture of glass bricks and pavers, in conjunction with the manufacture of blown glass and modelled product. A slump glass tile process only requires an operating temperature of around 700°C. Tiles can be made to order through a manufacturing and hand-painting process. Glass can be processed to size and stored for future use. It will cause no leachate problem, as the material is inert. Try to speak to an expert—a partnership with a glass artist is worthwhile because you can support and promote each other. Making simple glass products is relatively easy; making quality products is an art form, for which you need a great deal of skill and talent.

Processes to reuse your glass supply:

- **Manufacturing process for bricks and pavers**
  Speak to a glass artist about the potential for a basic glass brick and paver business with an association to the arts—it could be mutually beneficial.
- **Inclusion as an aggregate in other building mixes**
  This is simple solution, but it could be of great advantage to a local council or community group that wants to demonstrate their environmental credentials by building a local community or arts building from recycled glass with the design help of an artist.
- **Use of material for artistic slump glass processes**
  This isn't complicated, but it requires skill and attention to detail.
- **Manufacture of a bottle design to a specific low-pressure bottle industry, such as wine**
  This is an opportunity to produce a specific bottle for a wine making area—to make its product instantly recognizable in the market place.
- **Resale to processors for manufacture into glass products**
  The lowest-value endpoint for the product, but important just the same.

You will need:

- **Hand tools and safety gear**
  Goggles, full-face mask, gloves of various grades, sheet-glass handling equipment.
- **A hand-sorting line if material is to go back to the manufacturer**
  It is important to remove contamination, regardless of whether you are selling or keeping the material.
- **Glass crushers and screens to process material**
  Size consistency will be important to enable a number of uses.

- **A tumbler to produce decorative product**
  If you are intending to sell windscreen glass, for example, as a landscape product, you will need this to take the edges off.
- **Small-scale glass furnace**
  For foundry work; you will also need training to do this.
- **Moulding equipment**
  Your range of equipment should rely on advice from a professional.
- **A forklift or loader**
  This is imperative; its size depends on the size of your bulk bins.
- **Bulk-material handling containers or concrete bunker bins**
  Shipping container suppliers or the company to whom you are selling will provide these.

9. CERAMICS, CONCRETE, AND DEMOLITION MATERIAL

Ceramics come in a range of products, from broken plates and saucers to toilet bowls. Anything in unbroken condition can be resold. The process used to crush ceramic is the same one used to demolish concrete, asphalt, roof tiles, and bricks. The material can be processed in separate streams or, if you only have small quantities, collectively. If it is not used separately as a decorative landscape stream, all of this material, if sufficiently crushed, can be used as rock dust in the laying of poly pipe for drains, as a substitute for sand. It can be used for footpaths and as infill in bridge and road construction. You will find that there are engineering standards that must be met if it is to be used in a regulated area—be sure to check before you start work. The equipment for these processes can be large and expensive. You can store your materials and arrange for suitable equipment to be brought to the site when sufficient work is available, however. Engineering specifications are available for the reuse of these materials is various applications. Be sure to check.

Processing methods:
- Material crushing for landscaping, including tile and bricks—color-separate to red (brick), grey (concrete), black (asphalt), and white (china), then crush and screen

These can make a very attractive surfaces if designed with the help of an artist. I have seen them used in paving areas with old tools set into the paving. This serves the dual purpose of telling people what the surface is made from and giving run to your artistic bent.

- **Roadbuilding—crush and screen coarse materials**
  Again, refer to any existing specifications and requirements.
- **Clean fill—mix all types, then crush**
  This is not too demanding if the area is not for vehicle traffic but check regulations in any case.
- **General-purpose aggregate—mix all types, then crush and screen**
  This can be successfully used in concrete for a number of purposes.

Processing equipment:

- **A large hammermill or crusher**
  This is expensive equipment, but it may be available second hand, or you could hire it for the period needed.
- **Screens**
- **Conveyor belts**
- **Magnetic extractors**
- **Loaders and/or forklift**

10. SOIL AND CLEAN FILL DIRT

The term "soil" is very broad and can include everything from a quality topsoil to heavy clay, depending on whether you are buying or selling. Keep your soil near your compost operation—you can come up with some designer mixes to suit almost every customer.

Products and processing methods:

- **Clean topsoil**
  Reuse as-is for a range of purposes.
- **Contaminated soils**
  You can clean up some contaminated soils using bioremediation.

If the contamination is relatively low, you may be able to allevi-
ate the problem by dilution through mixing. Take care that you
know what you are dealing with. If you are not sure, get professional advice.

- **Graded subsoils and rock**
Screen and move rock to your concrete and demolition area.
Blend with humus-laden compost to produce a mineralized
soil blend.

You will need some or all of the following:
- A large hammermill or crusher
- Screen or a trommel
- Conveyor belts
- Magnetic extractors
- Loaders and/or forklift

11. MOTOR OILS

Used motor oil can be collected, held in storage, and refined to
build its viscosity back to its original standard and purpose. Dumping
it into the environment can obviously do substantial damage to
waterways; only tiny amounts are required to contaminate a water
table. Pressure on government needs to be maintained to ensure quality reuse for all collected motor oil. Depending on the region where it
is collected, clever thinking may be required to aggregate the motor
oil to a central location.

The most obvious needs in the longer term are to either recycle
the oil or to dissipate its effects in the local environment. Recycling
of motor oil requires a stringent process if it is to be used again in
machinery, and this is out of the question unless you can find some
way of aggregating it for transport to a larger town for reprocessing.
You could use old drench containers if you are in a sheep or cattle area.
Empty the containers (usually made of high-density polyethylene—
HDPE—these days) and triple-rinse them as you would in any drum

recycling scheme, then fill them up with used oil as you service your vehicles. When they are full, drop them off for recycling.

Products and processing methods:

- **Collection**
  As mentioned above, you will need to get the oil to a single collection point by a number of possible means.
- **Separation and filtration**
  This is usually done by the oil recycler.
- **Chain bar oil**
  An alternative is to filter the oil as much as possible to take out any impurities, then bottle it and use it as chain bar oil in chainsaws, which don't need new oil for lubrication.
- **As an addition to diesel fuel**
  If you are using a stationery diesel engine to generate power in a remote location, you can cut you diesel fuel with oil and burn it in your engine. This will dissipate the effects of the oil in the broader environment and, because the contaminant oil is spread thinly, the local environment will deal with it biologically in small amounts.

Processing equipment:

- **Collection tanks and vehicles**
  A professional collector will provide these if you have sufficient oil—contact your nearest oil recycler to find out if this is the case. You will also need a tank of some form if you are separating oil and contaminants for your own use.
- **Water separation tanks and processes**
  Again, contact a local collector or simply use an old tank and let it sit undisturbed to separate oil and water.
- **Pumps and filters**
  These will come from the same sources as those above.
- **Safety gear**
  Goggles, gloves, and breathing apparatus if the oil is contaminated, but don't take the chance—always use safety gear.

12. COOKING OILS

There are some good markets for cooking oil, but these are often limited to large urban areas. Landfill operators in smaller centers have found that the increasing interest in biodiesel has resulted in much of their cooking oil disappearing into smaller diesel processes. Information on these processes can be obtained from biofuels groups or from the internet.

Very small quantities of cooking oil can safely be included in home composting operations, but care needs to be taken that they are not overused. The alternative, when the quantity gets too large and regular, is to find a biodiesel maker who will take it off your hands or perhaps trade you fuel for oil.

13. CHEMICALS

Chemicals, by their very nature, are one of the most difficult problems for recycling efforts. As materials percolate downward they mix together, complicating the separation process.

Many communities now have government-provided toxics collections. Some of the more innovative have a chemical exchange program for less toxic stuff. Examples of such programs include Ecocycle in Boulder, Colorado, or the original Toxics Taxi in Sudbury, Ontario, which has now been copied by a similar operation in Sydney, Australia. Environmentally it is far cheaper in the long term to collect these materials up front than to have to deal with toxic leachate.

Products and processing methods:

- **Collect and securely store all chemicals**
  Regulatory authorities have standards and designs for storage of these materials. It is best to follow the regulators' instructions, but keep in mind that many people are willing to take partially unused bottles of many non-toxic chemicals, such as cleaning products.
- **Household paints—both oil-based and acrylic—can be resold to the public**

There are many paint recyclers around the world now, and a lot of information on processes is available via the internet.

You will need:
- **A controlled shed for the storage of dangerous chemicals**
  This will need to be constructed to safety specifications and regulations—check before you start.
- **A comprehensive range of safety equipment to deal with a range of products**
  Gloves, goggles, storage areas, and a clear list of emergency instructions in case there is spillage.

14. SALVAGE AND RESALE
One of the best markets for its investment of time and effort is the resale of materials directly to the public. These operations can successfully operate within cities of almost any size. They do take a great deal of knowledge, experience, and skill to operate successfully and profitably, and if you are thinking of getting into this area in a big way, look up some of the more experienced operators around the world, such as Urban Ore in Berkeley, California. Consider hiring them as a design consultant—the investment will pay off.

Several operations in the US, Scotland, Wales, and Australia have very high employment levels for small tonnages of recovered materials and very high financial turnover. Products sold can include almost anything and everything that was once in the community. Labor can be successfully utilized by dismantling unsaleable products when sales are slow, especially in situations where window glass, timber frames, doors, and jambs are of historical value and someone its renovating with a view to restoration.

Products and processing methods:
- **Reusables and repairables**
  Grade and market these via different types of resale stores. Depending on the size of the operation, a resale yard can have a variety of departments, and sale price can depend on quality.

- **Reusable building materials**
  You can sort, grade, or resell. Be sure to display goods where they can be seen—items buried under other items can't sell.
- **Reusables and spare parts**
  Machines and similar items that don't sell can be dismantled and sold for parts. These items can include cars, refrigerators, windows, window glass, door jambs, etc.
- **Reusable parts that don't sell**
  Scrap them into various metals and plastics categories and sell them to appropriate industries.
- **Batteries**
  A broad range of batteries can be refurbished and recharged for reuse or recycled through local government and other regulatory agencies.

You will need:

- **Hand and power tools appropriate to materials**
  You will need a full range, including battery-powered tools. Keep an eye out for older tools such as wood-working chisels, specialist planes, etc. It is wise to track materials by computer from the start, if possible. If this seems laborious, keep the long-term game in mind—tracking things that don't sell helps to rotate materials through valuable floor space and move them on.
- **Cash registers and a receipt program**
  It is imperative to be business-like about this. Make sure the receipt system tells you what you sold.
- **Racks, shelving, display cases**
  These items are often available at auction houses or sold in bulk when businesses close down, or from second hand outlets.
- **Forklifts and trucks for handling larger pieces**
  A quality forklift with extensive capacity is worth a great deal to the business.

Birds

She hit the windscreen – brakes applied
Driver thought of course she died
She tumbled backward from the car
And dumb and numb she hit the tar
We lifted her
The three of us
Black feathers white
Black road in light
And black wheels spinning out of sight

Her head, bent forward with eyes closed tight
Creating night and dazed with fright
We lifted her no human saw
The three of us now turned to four
We dropped her quietly into grass
To safely let the traffic pass
We all wait now to hear her call
Perhaps it happened
not at all

CHAPTER 5
The Future and the Road to Zero Waste

Various groups worldwide have taken up the torch of zero waste. But there is still much discussion in regard to what zero waste actually means. One thing that is sure is that there will be attempts by many companies to use the title to enhance their business prospects. Most of these operations are focused on a single product or process. For all these businesses' good intents, their activities may not necessarily be in the long-term interests of the zero-waste movement.

Schisms will occur in any new development as it struggles into the future. But whatever our battles and however long the trials and tribulations continue, zero waste must ultimately include every material thing. It cannot be an issue of what we recycle and what we do not.

… zero waste must ultimately include every material thing. It cannot be an issue of what we recycle and what we do not.

We also need to deal with the disasters, large and small, that we have created in the past. We must begin to live on the planet as if we were part of nature—a singular species occupying a niche, just like all other animals. And like all other animals, our relationship with nature must become seamless, or we will cease to be.

At a 2011 Zero Waste International Alliance meeting held in Puerto Princesa, the capital of Palawan Island in the Philippines, the assembled participants noted that repairing the soils of the world is the only viable answer to the issue of combatting climate change. Soils are the key to production of food, and their use and abuse determines the condition of our air, our land, and our seas. Changes in production methods that restore our farming lands and forests are fundamental to our long-term survival as a participating member in the family of species that populate and add complexity and biodiversity to the planet. A recent paper by entomologist Dr. Rob Blakemore shows that we have far more soil on earth than previously thought. This increases our capacity to store carbon through sequestration and soil management.[29]

There is much new science that needs to be applied to the recovery of human-made products. Indeed, there is much old science that needs to be re-applied with new eyes and a new perspective—a perspective not only on the damage we have done, but also on how we might apply both new and old concepts to achieve some variance in results. In a discussion with colleagues several years after the Palawan experience, and as the complexity of the issues became more obvious, it became clear that there would be many longer-term pollution sources that would require repair and indeed restoration. As an example, concerns are often raised of the contaminant levels of biosolids produced in many dense, urban societies. It is imperative, given their high levels of nutrient, that these materials are returned to the nutrient cycle at some point. Be that in forestry or in food, we must find some way of processing these materials to enable them to return to the natural cycle. I do appreciate that there are grave concerns in regard to antibiotics and other compounds contained in some of these biosolids. However, in many "waste" circles, all biosolids are condemned on the scant evidence provided by a few examples; and in any case, the nutrient cycle cannot be deprived of valuable material simply because it is contaminated. The question must be, 'How do we safely decontaminate these valuable materials to return them to the circle of life?'

When the old industrial areas of Homebush were selected for the site of the 2000 Sydney Olympics, much was made of the severe

29. Robert J. Blakemore, "Non-Flat Earth Recalibrated for Terrain and Topsoil," Soil Systems 2, no. 4: 64, https://doi.org/10.3390/soilsystems2040064/.

contamination of the site. However, it was found that after large-scale application of a range of organic mulches and composts that much of the contamination could no longer be found at dangerous levels. This is not that unusual. There are a number of companies around the world that sell biological products that process what humanity perceives to be waste but which the biology perceives as food. When sullage ponds were cleaned out at the Belconnen landfill in Canberra, the mixture, which consisted of sump oil, contaminated water, septic pump outs, and other indescribable liquids, was mixed with green waste, to which was added a biological mix. This had been bred from species found under and around old service station fuel and oil tanks. The biology chomped away for several months, after which time we took the partly composted or processed product and fed it to earthworms. Despite the fact that the material still had a strong petroleum odor, the worms consumed it. It must be remembered that hydrocarbons are a natural organic occurrence; if we provide a broad-enough biological base, nature will process it.[30]

Contamination is a multi-faceted and major issue for the zero-waste movement. In the main, contamination occurs in materials collections for roughly the same reasons it happens in other public spaces: poor management practices, poorly applied science, regulation that does not have environmental protection as its focus, and an attitude of disregard for the qualities of the spaces in which we live. Some elements of this expansive issue can be covered by environmental regulation, but unfortunately the greater part of the matter is ignorance of the effects of our own actions on the environment and a lack of respect for the individual demands we place on air, water, and soil. Why do people in developed countries have such a poor personal grasp of the implications of their own actions?

Contaminating the environment is not exclusive to the wealthier societies. Indeed, the paralyzing effects of plastic in and on the environment are being felt in every part of the world. Plastics have leached

---

30. Bryant N. Richards, Introduction to the Soil Ecosystem (Harlow, U.K.: Longman, 1974).

into our food chain with surprising ease, due in great part to our inability to contain the outputs of our own commercial greed. Having said that, the ubiquitous plastic bag, as said elsewhere, could be readily utilized to gather all forms of contamination if it were used as omnipresent infrastructure rather than regarded as the ultra-contaminating threat it is today. Its cheapness has led to it being used in every human community and in every economy for everything from a water carrier and food basket to a portable toilet, depending on circumstance.

I am not a great lover of plastic specifically, but it does have many practical uses. While it is clearly the scourge of the sea, it could also be its savior if its use was applied intelligently and comprehensively. Nothing is inherently evil—it is how we apply the gifts we are given that both our humanity and our intelligence will be judged.

As previously mentioned, when Typhoon Ketsana, known in the Philippines as Tropical Storm Ondoy, struck the Philippines three times in 2009, it was estimated at the time that around 40 percent of the devastation, including a great many of the human drownings, were caused by plastic bags blocking drains. But was that the fault of the plastic bags or of how the plastic bags were used? In communities where plastic bags have become endemic and currently cause irreparable damage, which is just about the entire world, they could become a valuable piece of infrastructure if the technology were correctly applied. A very large percentage of the world's population, about half, unlike most people trying to implement zero-waste policies, live in poverty. They don't have big shiny garbage or recycling trucks rumbling past their slums, emptying their big co-mingled plastic containers. What they do have, due to the greed of the Western financial model, is the plastic bag—in vast quantities. But applied intelligently, as in places like Curitiba, the plastic bag can be used as a vehicle to clean up communities, reduce health risk, and, dare I say it, recycle! There is a great fault among communities in the wealthier parts of the world to either assume that everyone has the same garbage service or to naively attempt to provide it to everyone.

If people in poorer communities were paid a small amount, on a sliding scale, for every plastic bag full of source-separated, clean, compostable organics, recyclable materials (like clean plastic bags), and residual waste (like dirty plastic bags), entire areas could be cleaned up. Community health would be improved, and the poor could generate income to allow them to buy food and improve their diet, saving the broader community health-services money—and all of this could be done using the plastic bag as a reliable but basic piece of infrastructure. If zero waste is to be implemented internationally, we have to get away from the imperialist attitude of being the only people in the world who have solutions to everything. The facts are that recycling services are available to a relatively small percentage of the world due to poverty as well as placement. Putting bins in every community in the world is errant nonsense.

Zero waste is a journey, not a destination; there is no simple solution. Banning plastic bags or putting a price on one tiny part of the material stream, like containers, become panaceas. They are not solutions or magic bullets—at the very most they address a few percentage points of the waste problem. In my own country, Australia, plastic bags amount to twenty thousand tons per year of a sixty-million-ton waste problem. You have to ask yourself if you want a band aid, a panacea, or a possible solution. No matter where you are in the world, in the bubble of your capitalist isolation, recycling your tiny little tin does nothing unless you see it as part of a much, much bigger picture. Fifty percent of the people alive on this planet currently live on around $2.50 a day. Zero-waste organizations need to be committed networks, providing the best skills and information to help others find their own solutions—not just another group of consultants with the answers to everything, who have never been outside their own countries' borders nor stopped to listen to the needs of others.

A true commitment to zero waste requires a focus on a standard that goes far beyond our day-to-day consumables. It must reach into every niche, waterway, and air pocket of our human economic model. Zero waste as a function of nature is as old as the planet itself. It is the way nature works and has always operated. There is no waste in nature. In nature, the outputs of one process are the inputs to another. Death creates life. But despite the fact that humanity is a part of the natural cycle of life and death, we seem to imagine ourselves beyond the bounds of nature. The base idea of an economy where wasted outputs are a sign of wealth is relatively new—not to mention unworkable on a planet with limited resources. So, the concept of moving back to a social and economic zero-waste structure in which waste is a dangerous aberration is both desirable and logical.

The first use of the term "zero waste" in relation to the general human waste stream, as far as I am aware, was when Lynn Landes established Zero Waste America in 1992. However, it is fascinating how the same or similar ideas come to the fore simultaneously. There have been a few instances of this synchronicity within the recycling industry over the past thirty years that I have been involved. Dr. Paul Connett, in his book, *The Zero Waste Solution*, mentions Arthur Koestler and his term "bisociation," which Koestler uses in his own book, *The Act of Creation*. It would seem that many people of like mind around the world simultaneously commenced a new focus on the value of recycling materials. Perhaps it is indeed this combined mass of many efforts and a rising awareness that has led us to this point. As noted by Dr. Connett, the first zero-waste community strategy was Canberra's "No Waste by 2010," which became policy in December of 1996.

"No Waste by 2010" had previously been used as a draft strategy title by the City of Newcastle, Australia, in 1994. A review was underway for their Summerhill Landfill but the name did not survive the draft stage due to nerves about the target and date. The notion of "no waste to landfill" was suggested by an attendee at one of the public consultations conducted by the Australian Capital Territory government after they heard about the Newcastle document title. The question was whether "no waste" was feasible, and of course the answer was "yes." This conversation made an appearance at every ensuing public consultation, and so the objective became a logical focus for the intention of innovative recycling at all levels.

Following the launch of the "No Waste by 2010" strategy, the concept of zero waste rolled very quickly into worldwide action. A group in California held a zero-waste conference in Monterey in 1997, organized through members of the GrassRoots Recycling Network and the California Resource Recovery Association.

Zero Waste New Zealand was registered as a trust in 1997 with the enthusiastic support of Warren Snow and funds from the Tindall Foundation, of which Warren was the manager. I joined the Zero Waste New Zealand trust as its founding manager. The long-term objective was to have New Zealand become the first country in the world to have a zero-waste objective in its national strategy—a goal that we achieved. But much of the ongoing work leading toward the national strategy was done by Julie Dickerson, who took over after I left. The objective initially was to develop progressive support from councils and to have them exchange ideas on successes and zero-waste programs. The first council to take on zero waste as its long-term goal was Opotiki in 1998.[31] Other councils followed, but the zero-waste target was eventually dropped from New Zealand's national strategy.

The multinational Waste as Resources Forum (WaRF) was established at Geneva in 1999 as an international body, supported by EMPA, the Swiss National Materials Testing Laboratory. At the time it was formed, membership was spread around the world and communication was difficult since the internet as we know it today was in its infancy. A board of management was established, but the only immediate means of communication were either telephone, which was expensive, or chat rooms, which were slow and painful, especially if those attending meetings had to get out of bed in the middle of the night to participate. EMPA supported the group with communications and staff, but the preparation of papers for the "R2000" conference in Canada simply could not be managed with everyone participating.

Consultant Rick Anthony of San Diego, California, became involved in the WaRF after the Canada event, and he also attended the Zero Waste Alliance establishment meeting in 2003 in Beaumaris, Wales. Anthony was invited to be on the Scientific Committee by a member of EMPA. Xavier Edelmann, who initiated the group, is still President of the Waste as Resources Forum. For those interested, Dr. Connett has produced the most precise and accurate history I have seen. It aligns well with my own recollections.

---

31. "Rubbish and Recycling," Opotiki District Council website, accessed 9 July, 2019, https://www.odc.govt.nz/our-services/rubbish-and-recycling/Pages/default.aspx/.

Most of the drive in the zero-waste movements now comes from the Zero Waste International Alliance and Zero Waste Europe. The latter has helped more than 350 communities in Europe put a zero-waste strategy in place. Of those, as of 2018, sixty-two had achieved over 80 percent diversion from both landfill and incineration and twenty-eight had achieved over 85 percent. These are very impressive figures when one realizes that Zero Waste Europe only really started functioning in 2011. The Zero Waste International Alliance and the Zero Waste International Trust (the latter intended originally to be a fundraiser for the former and registered as a company) were both formed in the UK in 2003 following the gathering of international representatives from seventeen countries in Beaumaris, Wales, in October of that year to investigate the potential expansion of zero waste around the world.

A primary objective of the zero-waste movement, implemented under the auspices of national groups, is to recognize that waste is a mistake that is generated by the careless use of resources. Zero waste aims to reverse this process and, through the careful use of resources, return the value and benefit of materials to local and international communities. There are many examples around the world where important jobs and family sustenance come from social discards. These range from the waste pickers in India, South America, Africa, and the Philippines, whose resource recovery work has become the direct means of income for a vast number of families, to the source-separated collections in Wales and numerous other cities around the world. All of these people demonstrate the value in the discarded materials of humanity and the potential benefit to local communities in recovering this value for employment and beneficial local use. Zero waste is a journey with many paths, and the one main thing that holds the zero waste family together internationally is the history of the movement. Any lack of recognition of this history belittles the whole notion and the work of many. The credibility of the movement is built on its history; regardless how innovative one individual may think their part in it may be, it belongs to everyone in the world, as it must.

CHAPTER 6
The Need to Regulate

"If you don't deal with climate change, all else is useless"
—Professor Ove Hoegh-Guldberg

Professor Ove Hoegh-Guldberg is the director of the Global Change Institute and professor of marine science at the University of Queensland in Brisbane, Australia. His is a long-time Great Barrier Reef researcher. In his early career he discovered the molecular mechanism behind coral bleaching, which—among many other indicators in our oceans, sky, and earth—is urgently telling us that we need to change our direction and attitude toward the planet. Grasping our connection between the bleaching of coral reefs and the deterioration of the environment through the overuse of chemical farming highlights the importance of understanding that our attitude toward the entire environment must change. If we cannot do this through respect and appreciation, then it must be done through regulation. This is particularly relevant in wealthy, disconnected, and unaware communities.

our attitude toward the entire environment must change. If we cannot do this through respect and appreciation, then it must be done through regulation.

While there is always resistance to the notion of regulation, we use it constantly on our roads, in building construction, and in community relationships. It is not a new concept, but the overriding threat of environmental collapse makes it imperative that we take a new approach to all aspects of the environment.

The Recycling Movement

The recycling movement has saved many millions of tons from landfill and incineration and has created many jobs with a range of local programs. Indeed, recycling industries have grown so much in the United States that they are now four or five times larger than the combined waste industries. Yet civilization today is still rapidly destroying its ability to sustain itself in a series of steps that show all the signs of being carefully choreographed. These steps are measurable, tangible, and obvious by notable factors: the waste we produce as pollution in our air, poisons in our waterways, and toxic waste from incinerators and landfills as it continues to increase.

Those of us who work in the resource recovery movements need to have clear objectives. If we are to hand something of a sustainable future to our grandchildren, it is time to move on from the self-congratulatory era of talkfests on waste minimization to an era of rapid social reassessment and on-ground activity. We can no longer be distracted with minor achievements, such as local recycling levels reaching 30–40 percent in developed communities—places that only represent 10 percent of the world population. We can no longer satisfy ourselves with increasing the profits of container manufacturers by recycling aluminum for them or by assisting the paper industry's environmental image by handing back their newspapers at less than cost. For humanity to survive, we need to redesign many of the things we make and use. If we continue extracting materials from nature for manufacturing, recycling these materials, then remanufacturing only 20 percent of what we recover, we are simply postponing the inevitable and curtailing the calamity. We need a new direction that can lift us all from the recycling and reuse treadmill and take us to another starting point in human history.

There is an increasing environmental awareness in communities and a willingness to participate in corrective actions. This is reflected in worldwide recycling surveys, which reveal that any surveyed community is willing to recycle. In the majority of instances, 90 percent of people are willing to do so. This is also reflected in the success of recycling systems in Wales and the zero-waste communities in Europe, where diversion rates from waste are skyrocketing and community engagement and excitement have become integral parts of resource recovery strategies. However, given that a 30–40 percent recycling level is still common in many other countries, it is clearly not the will to recycle that is the problem—it is the system in use. These systems feature poor design, inefficient collection processes, negative media reports, poor quality outputs, lack of positive beneficial feedback, packaging design that is complex and confusing, and incorrect and misleading markings.

At the moment, we have a waste handling system in which waste is 100 percent subsidized and recycling is the poor cousin—in the vast majority of instances, it is a poorly planned, ineffective, and expensive poor cousin. If recycling is to be the number one priority, what is needed is a resource handling system specifically focused on recovering all that it can, maximizing quality of material, minimizing damage, maximizing employment, minimizing mechanical handling, and focusing on value to the community rather than narrowly defined economic cost. In short—the Welsh model!

Restructuring Regulation

What would happen to recycling levels if the roles of waste management and the recycling industries were totally restructured? What would happen if the entire focus of both industries were brought into one focus of resource recovery that was as much a part of production as manufacturing? What would it look like if systems were redesigned to maximize the quantities of material recycled as a matter of course, if they were given a new and a vibrant focus?

If one is to look for benefits in a system, it is appropriate to think through the ramifications of the removal of any one element from the mix and its effects on the materials remaining in the system. The ramifications of source separation—partial or total—of all or any part of the mix of materials will determine the technology required to collect, transport, process, and add value to the final product prior to sale. To do this, we need to look at all elements of the system: collection, processing, sale, and reuse. We need to evaluate aggregation of the materials streams, both as a range of products and as a regional business opportunity.

We also need to fully evaluate the benefit and costs of all these elements in the final sale, including social values such as employment, community benefit, and environmental benefit. We need therefore to identify one-by-one the extraction of any one element from the materials stream and evaluate the effects of that removal on the value and handling properties of the remainder. But we also need to be cognizant of the loss of opportunity inherent in valuing only one small part of the stream.

The elements of any stream of output materials will vary depending on climatic conditions, eating habits, local supply, and other factors.

In the main, however, a few percentage points at most will be toxic materials, 40–70 percent will be organics, and the remainder will be basically inert. Of all the elements in the domestic material stream, the organic fraction is the most underrated, undervalued, and feared.

All of these issues can be overcome, though. It is true that organic material can have odors if allowed to rot. It can also be dangerous to health if not collected in the correct manner, and it cannot be successfully composted if it is contaminated. However, if correctly collected, processed, and utilized, it also represents the greatest opportunity and value of any waste material.

If the legacy emissions currently in the atmosphere are to be addressed, success will rely on the ability of the sea or the soil to absorb a very large amount of carbon—and we have little control over the sea. Improving our soils and changing agricultural practice to a regenerative or holistic model worldwide is a very important method of impacting on climate change, so the return of organic materials to soil is imperative. While climate change may be the largest threat we have brought upon humanity, the lifting of carbon levels in agricultural soils, increasing moisture infiltration, and the opportunities for change that it brings could be one of the greatest shifts that humanity has created since the start of the industrial revolution. This new direction is based on the simplest and most disregarded of the byproducts of humanity: our organic waste, in all its forms. Our ability to return organics to our soils must be driven by regulation—it is too important to rely on goodwill alone.

Examples from around the world in this field already exist. Regulatory models are in place in Scotland and the US. However, as we have seen in recycling, the system cannot rely on one process, one input, and one output. Whatever means are used in your part of the world it must be culturally and socially appropriate. In 2011, Australia introduced the Product Stewardship Act. To date it has been applied to TVs, computers, tires, mattresses, and a few toxic products. However, the big opportunity is to use the legislation to control the flow of organic waste back to the country's soils. The objectives are the logical control of organic waste—not to commandeer public input, but to engage community support and protect it. The potential reuse of organic material provides similar opportunities in any part of the world.

In Australia in 1999, CSIRO, the national scientific research organization reported that the country was losing $750 million worth of soil every year in the Murray Darling Basin due to soil degradation. As of yet there has been no indication in any of the scientific literature that this situation has improved. In fact, current indications are that degradation costs $2.5 billion per year in lost production. The Murray Darling basin is responsible for more than 40 percent of Australia's agricultural outputs. Despite the worrying implications of its degradation for the national economy and trade, this statistic seldom arises in the social conversation regarding preservation of either the Murray River system or our agricultural soils. In the main, the public seems unaware of any potential threat to their food supply, farming, or exports—the basis of the very economy on which community depends. People in larger urban centers seem to have lost that most fundamental of all links: our connection to the soil.

The manufacture of quality compost and liquid products from source-separated organic waste and its return to the soil offers the potential to remake that connection. Not as a panacea to our agricultural woes, but as a starting point to a national and potentially international discussion on food and the soil it comes from. Every individual produces organic waste, which is dealt with through domestic and commercial collections. Properly managing these collections is the key to remaking the human link to the soil. In Australia we have the legislative tools in place to assist such a process, but we need first to identify the players who can make it happen. The Product Stewardship Act has been a point of discussion and dispute in waste industry conferences and waste industry media over past years. The Act could make Australia a world leader if it were applied logically and thoughtfully to the serious issues associated with organic waste in Australia. Others have done it—why can't we?

Starting in January, 2014, all commercial businesses in Scotland were compelled to recycle metal, plastic, glass, paper, and cardboard. In addition, businesses producing over fifty kilograms of food waste per week were compelled to present this organic material, source-separated, for collection. The Product Stewardship Act in Australia could have the same focus, applied logically and on a national level. The waste industry, like any other, is resistant to any form of change. The large international corporate structures that dominate the waste industry are not dissimilar to any other large government or private agency. Change brings insecurity and fear. However, if change is of a legislative nature, it brings with it compliance as well as a level playing field. It also creates many more jobs and new opportunities. The difficulty facing all of us in Australia is that 75 percent of our agricultural soils, according to the New South Wales Department of Primary Industry, have less than 1 percent organic material in them. So there is a clear need for clean organic material to be returned to the soil.

Australia spends $11 billion per year, according to the federal Department of the Environment, managing more than sixty-four million tons of waste. Of this waste, more than 70 percent on average is organic material, if you include paper and cardboard. You would think that given the condition of our farming soils, the return of clean source-separated organic material to our food production system would be a no-brainer. It has also been proven in the City to Soil collection system, with its insignificant contamination rates of less than half of one percent, that this is not difficult to do with community support. Organic material is both the highest percentage of our waste streams and the largest single opportunity for community engagement, additional industry business development, increased employment, and successful diversion. The question, of course, is, "Why aren't we using legislation to ensure all organic material is source-separated, composted, and returned to soils?"

Successes with domestic organic collections such as City to Soil indicate strong community support for such a policy when it is implemented with a good engagement strategy. Even with the most whiz-bang engineering it is impossible to make clean, high-quality compost from the inputs of alternate waste treatment technology. However, it is now indisputable that if you use a clear community engagement strategy that tells people you are going to put their organics back into farms to grow food, you will get clean, uncontaminated materials in collection bins. In all instances where this engagement strategy has been used, the result is the same: clean organic product. The awareness of food production and quality is rising dramatically in Australia, and the ability to redirect organic waste as a clean, source-separated, high-quality composted product is surprisingly simple and somewhat obvious.

Utilizing the Product Stewardship Act

If this engagement strategy was supported federally by simple direction under the Product Stewardship Act, the entire industry would shift to develop new business models to suit. In Australia, collection, composting, and delivery of organic material is cost-competitive with landfill and will produce far better outcomes. Diverting all of Australia's organic waste into high-quality, biologically dense, composted or liquid products will dramatically raise the urban population's awareness of the needs of farmers as our food producers. The project is also transferrable, allowing for the cultural differences of any community in the world.

The Product Stewardship Act, working on behalf of all Australians, could direct the following:

- All councils must include a source-separated food and garden organic collection in the requirements for all domestic or commercials waste tenders.
- Clean, collected organic material must be composted on licensed premises, to the National Compost Standard, with specific nutrient and biological levels.
- All finished compost must either be used internally by council staff or delivered to an agricultural property within 200 kilometers of the council of collection.

With current landfill costs constantly on the increase and the value of vacant landfill space rising exponentially, such a program is more than cost competitive with the current rates-subsidized landfill process and would deliver better community outcomes, reduced landfill pollution, and reduced agricultural input costs. Such a program, rolled out nationally, would also put the issue of food production firmly on the Australian political agenda. It would be supported by a large number of farmers' associations and grower groups. It would readily fit with youth employment and training programs in remote areas and with natural resource management projects throughout the country. Australia has the need, in many areas, for the reuse of organic waste, but the elements that are missing are the collection imperatives and the end markets—both of which could be resolved using the existing Product Stewardship legislation.

Several years ago, in a presentation at the annual Waste Conference in Coffs Harbour, Australia, Grahame Collier, a respected educator and a member of T Issues Consultancy, pointed out that Australians began recycling in earnest about the same time they started using seatbelts in cars to save lives. Compliance with the mandatory seat belt law is now around 98 percent, whereas compliance with recycling is only around 40 percent. The only difference between the two is regulation. It is clear that if we want to reduce organic waste and increase diversion of materials, we need to take responsibility for the outcome using regulation.

"If you do not change direction, you may end up where you are heading."
—*Chinese philosopher Lao Tzu*

CHAPTER 7
Organics Options

In the region where I live, in the tablelands of New South Wales, many of the soils have been abused through the use of European agricultural systems and the desire for immediate profit in preference to long-term viability. I do not mean to say that this agricultural abuse was intended—as in most colonial expansions around the world, local indigenous practice was not considered, and whatever happened in the home country was put into practice in the new place.

As a result, though, we have extensive areas of land that were poor prior to the arrival of the Europeans and an even larger amount of land that has been abused into biological impotence. Living in the midst of such a landscape, it seems a relatively simple concept that this country would benefit from an increase in soil organic matter.

... one of the largest sources of organic material in this part of the world is what we often classify as waste.

Extending this a little further in the pursuit of possible sources of soil organic matter, it quickly becomes clear that one of the largest sources of organic material in this part of the world is what we often classify as waste.

The waste industry as we know it today is a relatively new business in terms of its size, financial base, and physical processes. The great majority of materials management was previously handled within and by each community. Today's model, in which giant cartels run contracts worldwide, is the product of shareholder profits. With a total focus on collecting as quickly as possible and on reducing any possible impact to community health, the industry has never in recent history taken much interest in the potential beneficial uses of organic waste. Also, it is not in the interest of the waste industry to make any part of their process simple. As previously noted, the more you mix materials together before you collect them, the more expensive it becomes to pull them all apart.

The importance of removing organic waste from urban situations to improve human health was realized in the late eighteenth century. As communities grew, more organic material was needed on farms to produce food and increasing quantities of urban organic materials began to be transported back onto the farms.

However, in the nineteenth century, as I have said, the work of the chemist Justus von Liebig and others demonstrated that crop production could be increased by the use of chemical fertilizer. In spite of the best efforts in the twentieth century of Sir Albert Howard, Lady Eve Balfour, Rudolf Steiner, and many others who supported biological processes, the profit-focused economy and chemistry, overrode common sense and scientific fact, and humanity began its ongoing work of soil degradation, erosion, land abuse, and declining nutrient values in our food.

More recently, when organic collections specifically for composting were developed, the focus was still one of simplistic waste management. The concept of higher standards for compost, in an attempt to remove poor-quality products from the market, made a difference. However, the waste and recycling industries have not put a great deal of thought or science into what alternatives may be possible to maximize the value of processed organic product—to use another methodology or process, to take it to another level, and to make something other than compost from organic waste. The same is true of all other materials regarded as waste. Very seldom do you find individuals in the industry who ask, "Is it possible to make something of more value from this product than what the product originally was?"

In addition to these issues, standards—as opposed to process—became confused in the minds of some in the compost industry. It was deemed that the only way to reach an approved standard was by using a very specific process. The concept of standards also confused regulators, and the objective of end-product quality became confused with how you got there. The modern waste stream is very different from what it was sixty years ago. Much more is discarded today. Our waste insanity is in part driven by the unthinking political obsession for a continually growing economy, based on a model of perpetual waste and continual renewal. It was a common economic understanding in the 1990s, and perhaps still in some circles today, that a very wasteful society is an economically successful one. If we waste enormous tonnages of goods and food and have to replace them daily or weekly, it was thought, then our economy may be functionally perfect. Alternate models of economic efficiency that constantly reuse and remanufacture—the concept of a "circular economy"—have only just begun to resonate; they have not as yet reached into the current vacuum of political thought.

The problem with our current economic model is that it requires a constant drawdown of the earth's finite resources—a structural model that cannot be sustained in the long term.

Even the clever concept of a circular economy is still just a phrase. It is not yet understood that any two products in such a system might be able to produce a third, more valuable, one.

We seem incapable of looking at materials and products in discard streams in their elemental form and considering what new and innovative things could be made from them. A fine example of this, regardless of the circumstances, is that composting is generally seen as a waste reduction technique—few people see it as a value-adding process. Composting is process through which a highly valuable, functional, biological product can be made; when applied at almost miniscule levels it can greatly improve the nature of soil. The waste industry looks at organic waste as it does all other materials, though: as a principal profit center that is collected in one large bin, mixed with other materials, and sorted in a large facility. Such facilities are often called "dirty MRFs"; they have never been successful, and they generally produce a poor-quality organic product that most farmers would refuse to have on their land. In fact, the government of New South Wales has just made it illegal to use such material on farmland or at old mine sites. It is with a suspicious mind, however, that one might consider that the incineration industry may have pushed hard for this outcome, so that they can now say that all organic materials should be burnt! This outrageously expensive and mindless destruction, when our soils are in desperate need of organic materials, must be battled at all costs. We need to be constantly searching to return materials to the natural cycle, the same way nature does. Our processes should reflect this.

Processes

If paper and cardboard are included, organic waste can comprise up to 70 percent of material streams disposed of as waste; in some instances, this number can be even higher. The greatest disadvantage of organic waste is that if even a small percentage of it is food, this generally contaminates the rest of the materials. So the best method is to ensure that food is not mixed with other materials in the first place. Source separation is thus the key to successful and profitable management—not only of organics, but of all materials. There are many options for the processing of organics. One process, or a combination of processes, can be used to change the nature of the product to a different form. A solid can be converted to compost, and compost and other high nitrogenous waste can be converted into worm castings. A solid can be converted to biochar and mixed with biology to greater effect. Foods, including meat, can be converted to a liquid biostimulant hydrolysate that can be used to replace fertilizer. This means that a solid can be converted to a liquid that has a much higher stimulant value to a plant than the original material.

The first requirement is to identify the maximum value that can be obtained from the product and where you intend to use it. Can it in fact be made into a product of higher value and quality? What is the cost of the process? Is it better to simply mulch the product for general use? What is the optimum use of that product, given a specific cost? What are the implications in regard to regulations? The opportunities in Australia for reuse of organic waste are extensive because soils are very low in soil organic matter; the beneficial uses of organic materials as mulch or compost for council projects, for the community, and for businesses are extensive. The largest opportunity, however, is the potential to connect the community back to the soil through the collection and reuse of their organic waste. Councils use a lot of soil and mulch products in landscaping. Most of the time this product is purchased from outside suppliers. The question to ask is, "Can the output you have be used as a replacement for something that someone else is currently paying for?"

The proper application of any organic material that has been processed to be biologically active can decrease chemical input requirements and increase soil organic levels and soil carbon. It must be remembered that any collection, transportation, and processing system must comply with regulations and standards. Nevertheless, it is not that difficult to comply, provided you select the appropriate processes. Check with your local environmental protection agency in regard to regulations and exemptions before you or a local organization make any decisions or any commitment to purchase equipment for a specific process.

Organic waste can be treated by one or more of the following means:

- Composting with an aerobic process
- Composting with an aerobic and a fermentation process
- Processing anaerobically to generate gas, which can be burned to yield heat and power
- Mulching
- Vermicomposting (worm farming)
- Maceration and inoculating to create a foliar fertilizer
- Fermenting to create a hydrolysate
- Manufacturing an emulsion to use as fertilizer or foliar spray

- Shredding to capture proteins or create fertilizer
- Wood pelletizing for energy generation

Food Waste

One of the important issues associated with wasting food is the amount we purchase. A great deal of the organic material we throw away in the developed world is due entirely to over-purchasing and poor storage.

Governments, both local and national, are beginning to appreciate that the removal of food waste from waste collections directly impacts the quality of residual collected materials. Separation removes the "yuk" factor and greatly increases the commercial value of the remaining resources. Most people have not yet begun to appreciate the value of that product when put to beneficial use in food production. There is still the unfortunate concept that we are dealing with a low-value product, that what was done in the past is always the best option.

Depending on the application of relevant local regulations, food waste can be processed through a diverse range of methods, some of which can produce energy and end products to enhance soils and long-term food production. Of course, one of the best uses for food organic matter, like other materials, is right at the point where it becomes wasted. If you have soils into which it can be buried directly, or if you can process it into a foliar spray or a compost, all the better.

The quantity of organic material in most commercial hospitality waste streams is greater than 50 percent of the volume and bulk of material outputs. While waste reduction is an important issue, the costs associated with the collection and disposal of this output are increasing rapidly. And in most instances this waste can provide sufficient offset to pay for the costs of collection and the costs of processing. Indeed, with the correct balance in terms of nutrient and microbial activity, it is a very valuable replacement fertilizer product. The ability to generate and quantify the beneficial energy and possible agricultural products produced as a result of these organic collections has yet to be fully researched. Indeed, the disparity of local relevant regulations is so vast as to warrant the identification of alternate processes used for compliance purposes. The common point in all instances, however, is once again the need for an effective and efficient source-separation process to ensure both good quality and highest end-use. There are existing successful models such as the Cleanstream brand, which was registered in 1998 in Wales and adopted successfully by Gary Kelk on Waiheke Island, New Zealand. In addition, there is the existing City to Soil client-engagement process, which provides the right tools, information, and motivation to achieve very high source-separation standards.

In the UK, the Animal By-Product (ABP) regulations mean that food waste must be processed in such a way as to ensure community safety, following the concerns regarding BSE (mad cow disease). This means that in terms of immediate processing, the principal available option is processing through an Anaerobic Digestion (AD) plant for the generation of energy and later application of the resulting digestate to land. Any other process such as maceration or composting would need to demonstrate, through evaluation and testing, a reliable and consistent regime before such a process would be licensed under the ABP regulations. Alternatively, if a collection and processing system were used in a country where ABP-type regulations were not applicable, it may be possible to develop a business model incorporating appropriate testing and evaluation that could be implemented in other communities around the world.

The Human Diet and Connections to Soil

Those who pursue a fast-food, Western diet are in the middle of a food crisis. This is in part evidenced by the number of people who are grossly overweight in Western society. With these excessively fat and unwell people, eating poor-quality food, we are rolling toward a medical and diabetic crisis that will cost the world community much more than money. Farming techniques and the overuse of chemical fertilizer have ignored, at the expense of human health, the fact that plants require between sixty and ninety minerals, nutrients, and trace elements for healthy growth. Most industrial farming processes apply only three of four of these. Vast numbers of people are becoming aware of the falling nutrient content and general quality of our foods, which is directly related to the imbalance of nutrients in fertilizers. This increasing awareness of food quality is demonstrated by the number of people who are now getting their food from farmers' markets, Community Supported Agriculture (CSA) programs, and community gardens. Home gardener advisory groups and numerous small businesses designed to help gardeners are also popping up—further evidence of the desire for change in food production.

On top of this, to support their goal of reducing the amount of waste going to landfill, local government agencies in some communities have begun developing food and yard waste diversion programs. Unfortunately, these activities arise not from a desire to improve soil quality but from a waste-management perspective.

If real change is to occur, it must be driven by a more holistic and long-term perspective.

In the few instances in which these food-waste diversion programs have delivered community engagement programs focused on improving soil quality, food production, and an awareness of healthy food, the response in high-quality source separation has been remarkable. In examples like the City to Soil program, delivered with a story that connects people back to the soil using the right tools, motivation, and information, we have seen very high participation rates and very little contamination in organics bins. The City to Soil program attempts to reconnect individuals to the soil with a focus on human health. The message is simple, and the response is strong. This innovative program also delivers into the hands of the community the political power to make change happen. The awareness of this issue and the use of the high-quality, source-separated, uncontaminated product delivers back to the community the tools to help change the food production system. It demands that policies be put in place to fundamentally change what we produce and eat.

Providing the What, How, and Why

There are many decisions to be made before a materials collection system can be implemented. These include where and what will be collected, what sort of vehicle will be used, what sort of processing system is needed, if an MRF of any sort is required (it won't be if you are source separating), if a composting site will be necessary, and what regulatory standards will need to be met and with what licenses. In the midst of all this is the most important element: the engagement process. How will the people implementing the system communicate with the public who will be placing materials out for collection? It is crucial that people understand what is required of them and that they are interested and have the right tools, information, and motivation to do the source separation.

The method of collection, including the bin and the vehicle chosen for collections, affects the effectiveness of the entire process. It is important that the collection system suits the end use. Clean, undamaged, and uncontaminated product can mean better quality and quantity of product, and therefore better prices. Collection systems in Wales, in which materials are source-separated into bins by house-holders, means products are placed into the collection vehicle by hand, with little or no breakage and almost zero contamination. Rather than investing in huge and expensive trucks and an expensive and complex MRF, the investment can go into people and jobs and a very simple storage facility. Many recycling programs are dealing with high levels of contamination. This can be a fault, in part, that is built into the system design. If paper, glass, bottles, and plastics are all collected in the same bin, then compacted into a side-loader vehicle, damage to collected goods is inevitable, as are lower prices and poorer quality of the end product.

The success of recycling collections around the world is predicated on the amount of contamination present in the collection container. There are different collection systems, different collection contain-ers, different collection vehicles, and different collection objectives. In other words, if you are only collecting paper, you don't want glass mixed in; if you are collecting bottles and cans, you don't want food in with it. If you are collecting food, you don't want glass, and if you are collecting organic waste—or yard waste mixed with food—it needs to be very clean so it can be turned into compost to use in gardens and farms. When designing a collection system, the "what" is the type of material to be collected and the "how" is the type of collection vehicle. The most important element, however, is the "why."

In 1992 I was employed by the Australian Capital Territory government to oversee the community engagement strategy for a series of trials to evaluate a curbside recycling system for Canberra. I had previously been involved in a printing and publishing business in which the focus was often on how businesses stood out from their competitors— in other words, I advised businesses on why people should contract them in preference to others. The overarching branding developed for the trial, by local designer Carolyn Brooks, communicated to the participants why their involvement was important. The look and feel of communication needed to be very different to anything in use at that time in recycling in Canberra yet connected to existing programs. At the same time, it was crucial that people involved in the trials were made to feel proud of being leaders in recycling, not only in Canberra but in the world. They were pioneering a new system that would have the potential to create a new recycling model both for Canberra and for Australia—which ultimately it did. In the communications with homes in the trial area, the public was again informed, most importantly, why the recycling trial was being conducted, what was to be collected (bottles, cans, plastic containers, paper, and cardboard), and how it was to be collected (by a side-loader vehicle).

In 2003, while working for the New South Wales government, and again with designer Carolyn Brooks, the same "what, how, and why" approach was taken with the first City to Soil yard waste trial. The engagement strategy was clearly worked; contamination rates were well under 1 percent in most instances. When a larger four-council trial collecting both food and garden organic waste was commenced in 2007, the same engagement strategy resulted in a contamination level of around 0.4 percent.

Marketer and author Simon Sinek, in his 2009 publication *Start with Why*, confirmed that a strategy that first explains why you want people to act in a specific way or to buy a specific product works. He gives the example of Apple computers, which first tells the consumer the "why" in their product: that "everything they do challenges the status quo—that they believe in thinking differently." Their "how" is the elegance of their computer programming, and their "what" is that they make great computers. This same strategy for the introduction of City to Soil in the City of Armidale in New South Wales resulted in a very similar outcome of almost no contamination. Remember that a good engagement strategy is the key to low levels of contamination in any recycling program. I would argue that City to Soil is successful primarily because its engagement strategy gives the usual "how" and "what," but with a clear focus on the "why." City to Soil has demonstrated—in accordance with its tagline, "Be Part of the Solution"—that people will get involved in recycling programs as long as they understand why they are doing it.

Organic Waste as the Point of Engagement

Much of the story of greatest importance to humanity—the story of soil and its effects on our food supply—seems to have been lost in the economic and disjointed babble of production, process, and transport. There has been more than enough written to explain to us in great detail the mistakes we have made worldwide with soils and food production. These include the overuse of chemicals to increase production and control pests and disease, the connections between poor diet and health, the consequences of poorly researched genetic modification and disease epidemics, and the obesity plague associated with processed foods from such production techniques.

Over the past forty years, warnings on the quality and nutrient value of food have become more persistent and the sources alarmingly varied. Humanity needs a connection back to soil, driven by an understanding of the need for clean, quality food. Such a connection at a broad level would provide communities with the collective political power to enable us to force change in our food production systems. The steady increase in farmers' markets, the demand for locally produced food, the focus of the community on organic food, and biologically grown fruit and vegetables and free-range meats are all indications that communities are prepared—indeed, they are searching—for better-quality food. To reconnect the community with the soil as its mother, we need a point of engagement.

I believe that this point of engagement is organic waste, and I know from the community response we have had to date that people do understand the importance of quality food and therefore the need for quality soil. This is not only a very sound and logical argument, but it also provides a very strong and resonating "why." As we face the potential food and soil crisis in Western society, acknowledging that the public must be part of the solution, City to Soil demonstrates that the access point for public engagement is both cheap and available. Its management is already paid for and its availability is unquestioned. To enable the use of organic waste in this important role, we need to review what it is we are doing with waste, what others are doing with waste, and where we might take the issue for the benefit of the community. We must take on the management of waste as a community tool for local economic benefit and employment.

There may not seem to be sufficient organic waste from households or businesses to make a substantial difference to the amount of soil organic matter in agricultural soils as a whole. But every human on the planet, if they are eating regularly, will produce organic waste every day, and the benefits of this waste depends on how it is applied to the soil. There is sufficient organic waste from every human to allow them to engage in the process of soil restoration and food protection in their immediate vicinity. We have been able to demonstrate on numerous occasions that people will respond to a request to engage in the process of source-separating organic waste. A community engagement program must be structured in such a way as to enhance the message of soil protection and to reinforce the need for quality food.

CHAPTER 8
The Soil Is Your Mother

Soil is the essence of human existence. Humanity needs an essential connection to soil, and as community we can remake that connection through our organic waste.

Farming has many faces in the different countries of the world. It takes on the cultural, climatic, and social aspects of any community, and farmers grow crops that are suitable to the tried and tested local diet, the soil type, available rainfall, or other local needs. Techniques used in food production can vary from traditional hands-on processes such as composting and manuring to machine-dominated systems that rely to varying degrees on external inputs. A recent UN report stated that mechanistic, industrial agriculture was literally running out of soil under the current chemical regime.[32]

In addition, the World Wildlife Fund says we have wiped out 60 percent of all mammals, birds, fish, and reptiles since 1970. The abundance of flying insects, many of whom pollinate the very crops we eat, has plunged by up to three-quarters over the past twenty-five years.[33]

At the same time, the costs of agricultural inputs rise every year, so the costs of production, and therefore the costs of food, rise. However, if grown under the industrial regime mentioned above, it is arguable that the destruction of soil will ensure the demise of farming families as well as our food supply. Around 70 percent of farmers worldwide are subsistence farmers or small landholders. In poorer countries more than 70 percent of agricultural work is done by women. [34]

32. Chris Arsenault, "Only 60 Years of Farming Left If Soil Degradation Continues," Scientific American website, accessed 9 July, 2019, https://www.scientificamerican.com/article/only-60-years-of-farming-left-if-soil-degradation-continues/.
33. Francisco Sanchez-Bayo, et al., "Worldwide Decline of the Entomofauna: A Review of Its Drivers," Biological Conservation 232, https://doi.org/10.1016/j.biocon.2019.01.020/.
34. 4 per 1000 website, https://www.4p1000.org/.

These are crucial matters in regard to world food production. They directly impact the way in which we produce food from our soils.

At the other end of the conversation is the fact that many farmers, regardless of size, scale, and cropping regimes, have reduced their input costs dramatically and have changed management practices to provide profitable outcomes while still protecting their soils. Regenerative and holistic farmers have demonstrated the opportunity for change and the profitable benefits, both in terms of food quality and the environment, of continuing to battle against the mechanistic model of farming.

We All Eat

Regardless of how we live our lives in this world, we all eat, so it is crucial that we are aware of the issues that surround food production. We must engage the entire community, including those who live relatively dislocated in high-rise dwellings, in this conversation. Over many years, the education of farmers on the latest science or practice in farming was described as "extension." By this is meant "the application of scientific research and knowledge to agricultural practices." It seems odd that the agricultural practices that produce the food we eat never seem to include the full cycle of production—they mostly miss the most important element in farming: the customer.

The customer is the pressure point that can be applied both socially and politically to create change.

If we are to have a conversation about food production, protecting our soils, and our farming families, the customer needs to know the issues and how they can become involved. Factors influencing the criticality of their food supply, based on UN reports, include the chemistry used in agricultural production, the loss of insect pollinators, the species losses caused by uncontrolled fires, and the devastation caused to soils, oceans, coasts, and reefs by chemicals. On the beneficial side, customers need to also know of the potential role of regenerative and holistic farming and what the community can do to control prices, to identify clean food, and to reduce costs. If extension and education in food production and consumption is to exist in the future, it must go both ways—to households as well as to farmers.

Embracing the Food Movement

In recent media stories covering the rising interest in TV cooking programs, food quality, local markets, local production, and nutrient value, the collective food movement has been described as "the new rock and roll." Farmers' markets are now a standard event for any person with an interest in flavorful and nutritious food. In Western societies there is now an increasing array of farmers' markets, where the local population can purchase high-quality foods that remove the profit-taking of the middleman and correspondingly increase the return to the farmer. The demand for organically and biologically grown fruit, vegetables, dairy, and meat is on the rise, and this increase in sales has the potential to not only protect farmers and their investment but also to enhance the long-term qualities of our soils and our environment. The biological food movement provides the opportunity to link the farm movement with the quality of the food we eat. The growth of this process has made food the most easily understood example of the need for a circular economy, which Wikipedia describes as:

> An economic system aimed at minimizing waste and making the most of resources. In a circular system resource input and waste, emission, and energy leakage are minimized by slowing, closing, and narrowing energy and material loops; this can be achieved through long-lasting design, maintenance, repair, reuse, remanufacturing, refurbishing, and recycling. This regenerative approach is in contrast to the traditional linear economy, which has a "take, make, dispose" model of production.[35]

---

35. "Circular Economy," Wikipedia, accessed 9 July, 2019, https://en.wikipedia.org/wiki/Circular_Economy/.

There are many hands-on groups at the international, national, and local levels that have been established to support and enable food production to move back to a biological, if not organic, base. Many such groups utilize similar principles, drivers, and ethical standards. They wish to see the quality of what we eat, its price, and its delivery to the community as the principle criteria for the future of food—rather than the production costs, market capture, and profit model currently in broad use. Underpinning this wish is the need for increases in soil quality, biological diversity, and nutrient availability. This trifecta is the basis of the motto of soil associations around the world of "Healthy Soils, Healthy Food, Healthy People." For many years, the food movement has concentrated its efforts in lifting the awareness of the community of the need to demand better nutritional qualities in food and in reducing the use of chemicals in agriculture, weed management, and food processing.

The movement has also recognized the need to return organic waste to soils as quality compost in order to improve soil quality, diversity, and nutrient availability. For the Zero Waste International Trust (ZWIT) and like groups, this is the key to the front end of the food movement. The source separation of clean organic waste for ultimate application to soil as quality composted product is the key to the ZWIT food support policy. It seeks the support of organic, biological, and regenerative food production organizations that are seeking the beneficial engagement of the broader community in their programs.

Based at the impoverished end of the waste industry, many recycling programs, driven in part by regulation and in part by guilt, operate on the edge of resentment, especially if the person doing the recycling does not understand the long-term objective. If the householder sees that the long-term objective is simply making money for the large waste companies or those receiving the collected material, personal dissolution can often lead to poorer-quality recycling. However, if the householder is excited and involved in the collections program and feels that both they and their community are gaining from source separation, good results are almost inevitable.

Organic collections for the City to Soil program have concentrated on reminding participants of the importance of collecting the material clean so it can be used in soils to grow food for families and children; therefore, it must not contain contaminants such as glass, plastic, or metal. Contamination levels, while collecting with this understanding, have never risen above half of one percent. Source separation success indicates an understanding and commitment by households of the objective of clean source-separated organic waste for use in soils. More importantly, in areas where these collections have been successful, it would now be very difficult for such programs to be discontinued because, once accepted, they have become the "property" of the local community—they have become social capital, political capital, and, most importantly, local assets.

Local Assets, Local Benefits

The management of waste is a very expensive exercise for any community, yet a very high percentage of the waste stream, especially the organic "yuk" factor, once source-separated, can go into local soils to grow quality food. In most urban communities, a large percentage of total rates and taxes are expended on the management of waste. Any community that can use any waste materials locally, while not necessarily reducing waste collection costs, can reap real local benefits by treating these materials as local assets. Materials reuse can create local industry, increase employment, and—in the instance of organic waste—provide support for the production of local food. Local buy-in from local communities brings with it enormous social value and political power. Source separation of organic waste for use as compost underpins the importance of the food movement, the desire for quality food, and the need for reduced contamination. It enables the local community to literally vote with its food. As Wendell Berry notes in *The Unsettling of America*, "The soil is the great connector of lives, the source and destination of all. It is the healer and restorer and resurrector, by which disease passes into health, age into youth, death into life. Without proper care for it we can have no community, because without proper care for it we can have no life."

Waste and Our Organic Future

In 2003, the New South Wales Department of Environment and Conservation conducted a social research series. In their document, Who Cares about the Environment, people were asked to nominate the two most important issues for attention by the state government. The two social priorities and values of concern nominated by the vast majority were health and education. The environment rated as sixth and water eighth. There is no indication if any of the people questioned were aware of the interconnection between the quality of their health, the standard of education, and the state of the environment, or indeed the quality and quantity of water. In fact, the manner of treatment of each of these issues by the media, by government, by science, and by the bureaucracy means that each of these issues is treated in isolation, as a series of separate and unrelated entities.

John Hamaker noted in his book *The Survival of Civilization* that we are killing ourselves with specialization.

The ability to recognize that all things in nature are interconnected has been fundamental to the human ability to survive.

A reductionist approach to science in some areas has isolated specialist knowledge into specific fields of endeavor, where cross-pollination of scientific abilities is either dismissed or actively discouraged. There is little awareness at any level of the population that the quality of the environment, specifically the quality of soil, in many ways determines not only the quantity and quality of water but it also the quality of human health. We are what we eat.

Civilizations that have survived flood, drought, disease, and famine are those that have a reliable and consistent food supply. Those with a successful agrarian base are the ones that nurture their soils, caring not only for the plants but also for the biology of the soil, which stimulates the release of nutrients and maintains soil structure, secures carbon and moisture, and increases land value. Within this context, waste becomes a metaphor for our attitude to the planet. It is an "end of pipe" attitude that is reflected in our health, education, and prison systems. We cannot in all truth refer to our system of community care as a health system when its principal focus is on keeping people alive once they are ill. We spend the vast majority of money on sick people, not on keeping people well. We address only the symptoms of our disease.

Author Germaine Greer, in her attempt to restore a rainforest to its former self in her book *White Beech*, refers to the "fog of good intentions and phony positive thinking which allows the government to keep ignoring the real gravity of the situation." This same fog makes an appearance in many aspects of community, from recycling to homelessness. Many of our "caring" programs, such as overnight accommodation for the homeless, recovered food for the hungry, and container deposit systems, simply operate as excuses for our poor attempts to cover our own guilt. They are not addressing the actual issues. In countries as wealthy as ours, what we are not addressing is the issue of shelter, food, and waste, in real and functional ways. Why do we always dance on the periphery?

Waste, like illness, incarceration, and ignorance, is the result of a lack of care, and a lack of care is reflected in our attitudes to consumption. The structure of human values within Western society is bordered by parameters such as new or old, antique or secondhand, used and recycled. In most modern economies, many in the up-and-coming younger generations pursue the new in preference to the old—they must have the latest in all things, and asset gain is the principal social imperative. The driver is "more," and to have more is to be happy. While change appears to be happening among some younger people, it must become more widely accepted if we are to survive into a foreseeable future. In the current widespread model, more money equals more things, and more things equal more happiness. Our modern social context is predicated on getting what we want, not necessarily what we need. The corporate intent of the commercial world is to spread that same condition to the rest of humanity so that every human on earth can also get what they want and not necessarily what they need. This does not occur because of any interest in social justice or fairness or equity, but simply to ensure that the shareholders' investment in the corporate structure is constantly protected by creating new markets and generating more profit. In the creation of these new markets, the only obligation on either the corporate structure or its board of directors is to make more money for the shareholder. The shareholder, in turn, is comfortably removed from the day-to-day liabilities and any ethical responsibility for the behavior of the directors by simply declaring that their interest is purely the investment. Environmental groups constantly question this model, which is clearly eating the heart out of our potential to exist on the planet, yet we behave as if we are helpless to stop it. Indeed, the Western lifestyle in the main supports the very consumption that is destroying it. We have taken the Industrial Revolution to its logical consumptive conclusion by driving the principle resource inputs of the planet toward zero and raising the pollution levels to the maximum inhabitable levels.

Road Kill and Culls

There are many forms of waste in the community. In addition to the stuff you put into a bin, there is also commercial extravagance in its many forms, the costs of which are put upon the customer in the guise of normal practice. As a general rule, the bigger the "yuk" factor, the more expedient and wasteful the process for dealing with the material. One of the greater wastes in an omnivore-consumer-driven society are the remnant parts of animal carcasses.

Some parts of the world are notorious for road kill—animals hit by high-speed vehicles and left on the side of the road. These are a very good input sources for composting. By using the right combination of green shredded waste, inoculant, and a cover, you may even make a high-quality compost without the need for too much additional water. There is also the availability from time to time of animals killed to reduce population pressures on farms whose available grass will not support both an income and large wildlife populations. On top of this is the waste produced in the meat industry. If you like the notion of fresh meat on your plate, you may be unaware that the bit you eat represents only about one third of the animal. By removing the hide, bones, hoofs, horns, intestines, and tail, we throw away about two thirds of the average animal. Poultry processors generate an abundance of heads, guts, feathers, and feet. Indeed, in the egg production industry, the average chicken will slow in its ability to produce eggs after about three years. Even in the free-range world of egg production, there is no "happy valley" retirement village for unemployed chickens. They are eliminated, because egg production is a business, and chickens that do not lay are a non-productive liability to the business.

Leaving aside the conversation regarding eating meat and eggs from happy and contented animals, there is much waste in the meat and egg industry that could go back into soil given the correct biologically safe process or treatment. In fact, all bodies are packages of nutrients and can be biologically enhanced to create liquid biostimulants, foliar fertilizers, compost, and biochar of the most stunning quality—products that will make your veggies leap from the soil with vigor and vitality.

It is worth reinforcing the ancient notion that nature uses death as the source of life. The conversion of all this material into clean and safe products can rebuild soil into a healthy and resilient base for the production of fruits, vegetables, and grasses.

There are many other potential sources of death and decay that can provide inputs to soils and food production. In Australia we have very large populations of feral animals and feral plants, many of which are regarded as weeds. Collectively they cost the nation billions of dollars in control and lost production due to ecological destruction—yet they could be the very source of rural and regional employment for indigenous and non-indigenous people. They place a very large burden on the work of traditional owners, park rangers, farmers, and environmental groups across the country every year. In addition to the cost of feral management there are also the costs of social disruption, infrastructure damage and repair, and, in some instances, cataclysmic damage to native species. It is the same story in all rural areas, and the cost rises every year. Virtually the only control mechanisms available in the past were the direct activities of trapping and shooting by farmers and the ad hoc presence of fox hunters using high-powered rifles at a distance. At that time, both fox shooting for the purpose of income and pig hunting as sport were very prominent pastimes.

However, lack of negotiation with land owners, poor training, and control in the use and management of firearms restricted these activities to very specific areas. The fact that the great majority of hunting was conducted at night meant that these activities were clandestine, and any income or benefit to the broader community, when measured against cost, was questionable. When social mores placed pressure on the use of fox furs, the market collapsed and has not since recovered. While pig hunting is still in vogue with the use of dogs and guns, a lack of training and no business structure means the pastime has little if any measured effect on the feral pig population. In any case, many pig hunters regard it as their personal right to hunt pigs as sport and recreation, and pig numbers are growing due to hunters destroying government pig traps. The problem for park rangers, park managers, and farmers has grown exponentially, and the cost outstrips the problem at an ever-increasing rate.

Until such time as the problem of feral weeds and animals is structured in a business model, where the operation is a profitable activity, it will continue to cost Australia and other countries dearly in terms of lost native species, lost income, and lost opportunity. I realize that there is a general and, I believe, incorrect reaction from pest managers that utilizing feral species as fertilizer will ensconce them as a permanent base for soil fertility. However, unless we come up with something that significantly cuts their numbers, we will be pouring money into a feral hole from now until forever. Recent reports from parts of northern Australia place feral cat numbers at near plague proportions. While politicians make gross and exaggerated claims about what they are going to do to control these issues, their thought bubbles are never financially resourced, and in most instances, budgets are cut rather than expanded.

In simple terms, the fact is that these introduced species have simply occupied an ecological niche in the environmental structure previously occupied by one or more native species. These species use the same or similar resource inputs to build body mass and reproductive capacity through light, nutrients, water, and energy. They are made up of the same sugars, proteins, chemicals, and biological structures as native species. In the same way that indigenous peoples and farmers use techniques to manage species for their day-to-day existence by harvesting and taking products to market, so too can techniques be used to turn feral species into a valued asset, provided a market can be found for the outputs. The key to this conversation must be the holistic development of a harvesting, processing, and sales model that is supported by current economic practice. We already have available, cheap, and effective technologies to convert any organic material into useful and stimulating organic products for use in fields or forestry. Weeds species can be converted into a valuable compost product using a conventional composting technique. Recent local research has indicated that common fleabane and other noxious weeds can be used as a high-quality, on-farm biological input to help increase nutrient efficiency by delivering humus and carbon to soils. Several licensed compost facilities in New South Wales are now using a simple inoculant-based process to deliver a high-quality fermented compost, using food and garden organic waste as inputs under the City to Soil project. The inoculant product used to make compost is very cheap, is made from open source recipes, and requires no more equipment than what can be found in the average kitchen. The product will control odor in the compost manufacturing process and can be made in bulk quantities using any organic material as an input.

Despite assertions to the contrary by recycling industries, compost is only one of a range of products that can be made from organic waste—you can also make it into biostimulant liquid, worm castings, compost tea, fertilizer pellets, and biochar. Recent research has shown that adding the right inoculant product and water to macerated animal bodies can convert the end product into a viable foliar fertilizer product—similar in many ways to the emulsion end-products already on the market, but without added energy input. Liquid and solid product can be used in agricultural applications or in any pasture improvement process. Fur and skins may have markets in the felting and leather industries, and residual bone materials can be processed in either calcium-phosphate products or direct-drilled into soils as a conditioner. These liquid products, known more generally as protein hydrolysates, have an extensive and valuable role in horticulture and agriculture—not only as fertilizers, but also as biostimulants, having beneficial effects on abiotic stress factors and nutrient availability.[36]

The potential of these hydrolysates to partially or fully replace chemical products already on the market, or to use them in association with other known alternate products, is very real and provides the opportunity to develop extensive niche products for specific crop applications. The value of the end product in this process would mean that the person who delivers the animal carcass for processing could be paid an amount that reflects the sale value of the liquid product to farmers. This in turn would mean that indigenous people, living in their own lands, would be able to generate a viable income while at the same time managing the ecology of their own area in a more hands-on process. The control of feral animals could operate at a size and scale that would be able to support a large percentage of farmers' organic fertilizer demand.

The process of liquefying a product for use as a foliar spray will always mean that a percentage of solid material will be left behind. One possibility is to mix this product with a protein source such as the weed *Mimosa pigra* or common gorse *(Ulex europaeus)* to create a product that is dry enough to pelletize for potential use as a fertilizer or a feed. The opportunities are endless.

---

36. Giuseppe Colla, et al., "Protein Hydrolysates as Biostimulants in Horticulture," Scientia Horticulturae 196, http://dx.doi.org/10.1016/j.scienta.2015.08.037/.

CHAPTER 9
And Now ... the Future

Resource efficiencies, which go beyond linear systems and reflect the true cycles of nature, must ultimately be the way of the future if humanity is to survive in anything like its current form. It will no longer be enough to simply recycle goods back into like or similar products. Materials must repurposed in far more permacultural and regenerative ways, in systems that provide multiple benefits in a natural system.

To enable this transformation, value must be added. But it must be a broader value, one which adds concurrent levels of opportunity to both the asset in question and its place in its broader circumstance. In the same way that sea water, soil, plants and animals interact at a range of levels and provide multiple services in their broader environment, so any material that humanity guides back to the service of nature must be multifunctional and must add value in multiple aspects.

Returning products that assist plant growth must also be able to clean the air, polish water, raise humus levels, increase soil biology, stimulate yield and encourage diversity at every level simultaneously.

Until now, nature's services have been seen by humanity as goods to be plundered, structures to be stripped, materials to be mined and seas to be sullied. Yes, we have survived on nature's bounty, but in so doing we have damaged or destroyed most of what we have touched. We have eliminated fisheries and forests for want of careful management, cleared and destroyed rainforest and savannah for short-term cropping, and poisoned water tables, rivers and seas by overfertilizing those crops while endangering reefs and islands alike.

We are a part of nature, and it is inevitable that we impact it in some way. But does that impact need to be negative and constantly draining, or can we learn to take and return in a natural cycle of civilized sanity?

The advent of usable and practical wind and solar electric energy has clearly demonstrated that a new way for humanity is indeed possible. As John Hamaker described almost 40 years ago in *The Survival of Civilization*, we do have the ability to grow humanity into a species that can work with the earth for our mutual and sustained survival. We now have the tools to put back into the soils the nutrients we have depleted and rebuild their biological and structural integrity.

The potential to embrace natural processes and add to them value for humanity, without polluting the air, land and sea, has become a very real thing. The same is true with products we previously regarded as waste. In fact, it is waste that now becomes our salvation. For many years many of us have pursued the notion of adding sufficient value to waste materials so that they may become our way forward, our leading light. I believe this has now happened with organic materials. The implementation of the following concepts will require much change—especially among those of us who have stalled opinions in regard to resource recovery.

The evidence is now confirmed that this is achievable. We can now add more value to organic materials than we were ever able to add to the inert materials we have been sending off for recycling and remanufacturing.

These organic materials processing technologies rely in their essence on the cycles used by plants and biology for sustenance and growth. By working with these concepts, we now have the means to sustain agriculture with dramatically reduced costs, poisons, and chemicals. They provide the means for the farming family to retake the farm as their ongoing means of production and income.

In her 1997 book *Biomimcry*, Janine Benyus, reflecting on the make-up of plant structures, noted that there are up to "five hundred or six hundred different compounds in the same leaf, each with fifty or sixty different biological activities."

This same diversity occurs in the root microbiome. Microbes feeding on plant exudates produce humus. This in turn causes soil particle aggregation, allowing moisture infiltration from both rainwater above and groundwater below. Gerald Wiebe, a farmer in Manitoba, describes this as the integration of "physics, humus, and the water cycle."[37]

Organizations such as Green Cover Seed have demonstrated how growers can dramatically change the nature and structure of soils by utilizing the biochemistry of plants and the interrelationships in the root rhizosphere through the use of cover crops in a range of cropping and livestock integration systems.[38] The process allows farmers to access ecosystem services from living plants—capturing solar energy, increasing nutrient cycling, and supporting the water cycle—all through the stimulation of nature's biodiversity.

The following are descriptions of several rediscovered inventions for nature's organic materials and their impact on soils and soil structures.

SPICE, Quorum Sensing, and Autoinducers

The Static Pile Inoculated Compost Extension (SPICE) process takes composting a step further. It produces a useable and highly effective product for soils that is also a family of autoinducers. These can be safely extracted from the final fermented compost product as a fluid and applied to seeds prior to planting as an in-furrow irrigation and during tillering as a foliar spray. Autoinducers are a chemical-signaling molecule used to communicate cell population density. This ability leads to Quorum Sensing, which enables bacteria to synchronize the gene expression of the group, enabling unified actions.

The SPICE compost process enables the production of autoinducers in its fermentation stage and is initiated by an easily made open-source compost inoculant. This inoculant is a biological product that contains microorganisms that help to decompose and compost organic materials in low-oxygen conditions. The product can be made and stored easily on the farm. This inoculant is applied to the feedstock material as you are setting up a no-turn, covered compost pile.

---

37. Gerald Wiebe, "Physics, Humus and the Water Cycle," https://www.gerrygillespie.net/latest-news.html/, accessed 24 July 2019.
38. Green Cover Seed website, https://www.greencoverseed.com/, accessed 24 July 2019..

The compost inoculant is partly fermentation based. Fermentation is rich in autoinducers. This means that its microorganisms live in low or no levels of oxygen. These are the conditions that exist in the SPICE compost system, in which a waterproof cover is used to control the level of air and the pile is not turned. The aim of using the inoculant is to catalyze the process of composting in the pile and to ensure that the right community of microorganisms are doing the composting process. The biodiversity in the compost extract reflects the structure of the processes used to create the compost. So, the more complex the compost process, the more complex the extract. A compost that goes through both an aerobic and an anaerobic phase has the optimum opportunity to create the broadest possible microbial base.

Use of the combination of extract and compost has the potential to eliminate the use of inorganic nitrogen fertilizer in crop production and to return farming to a solid biological base. The reduction of cost to agriculture can help make farming in the future both economically and environmentally sustainable.

While composting has previously been seen by waste managers as a waste reduction process, the SPICE process has been demonstrated to create around 25 percent more compost from the same organic inputs as an aerobic process.

Biostimulants

Extensive research is now available on the use of biostimulants in agriculture, horticulture, and general gardening. A biostimulant is any product that will initiate additional biological activity. Several international biostimulant conferences, in combination with consistent research results, have raised the profile of the subject with farmers generally. Many biostimulants have a high level of autoinducers and are in use as both a foliar fertilizer and a soil drench. Many can be readily made on the farm. There is increasing evidence to support the use of biostimulants in a diverse range of plant species. The available literature also states that there are a range of positive responses to biostimulants, including increased yield and abiotic stress tolerance, increased root growth, and enhanced nutrient uptake.

The commercial value of biostimulants was reported to be increasing at a rate of around 12 percent per year. Organic material streams previously considered waste are readily converted by a range of processes into biostimulants, adding value and direct commercial application to products manufactured for collected organics—especially food.

Inoculant

An inoculant is essentially any product that introduces new microbial families to start a new process. They contain catalysts that can support processes such as the aforementioned SPICE compost system, the effects of which are a larger range of biological products that can help create soils dominated by fungi. They are cheap to make from local materials and have been readily understood for millennia. Variations on inoculant products appear in almost every culture around the world, from the vermicast solutions of the worm world to *Panchagavya* in India.

Hydrolysate

Biostimulant protein hydrolysates made from plants and animals are readily made organic inputs and as such are safe for the environment and will contribute to low-input, high-output crop production. Their use will help reduce the amount of chemicals used in agriculture and can simultaneously reduce waste to landfill. While large-scale commercial enzymatic processes are available for the production of hydrolysates, the process described here can be conducted entirely on the farm or in the home in almost any part of the world and at a very low cost, with few or no external inputs.

Hydrolysates are a very good substitute organic nitrogen source for farmers and gardeners wishing to move away from artificial nitrogen inputs. The process of hydrolysis denatures proteins back into amino acids and peptides, the amino acids being a readily available form of non-volatizing nitrogen. When applied in the form of a foliar spray, amino acids are taken up principally by the plant stomata, intercellular structures, and the plant roots. In achieving a low pH to ensure the destruction of the required range of pathogens, the pH at the completion of the process is at or below 4.6. This low pH is not a concern, as the product is diluted by a ratio of at least 100 or 200 to 1 prior to application using any standard boom-spray unit. This also means that the cost of manufacturing the product on-farm is relatively low and, more importantly, it can be produced and applied as required.

The Processing of Raw Waste Materials into a Foliar Spray

This simple process takes the raw products from a waste or feral animal source and converts them into a viable foliar spray that acts as a biostimulant to enhance crop qualities, nutrient efficiency, and abiotic stress tolerance. The process of lactic acid hydrolysis breaks proteins down into a range of amino acids, making them available to the plant through intercellular and stomata structures for uptake, growth, and support.

Breaking down these proteins, which can come from either plant or animal material, is achieved by macerating the material to the smallest possible size and then adding water, carbohydrate, and a base lactic acid mix. This liquid/solid mix is then fermented under a one-way airlock for a specific period to achieve conversion. During lactic acid fermentation, the pH of the mix decreases to a point at which a specified range of pathogens will not survive.

To ensure total processing, the mixture is left to ferment for four weeks. This time period may eventually be successfully modified depending on product input and output. Crop type, season, and application rate should always be determined under agronomic and agricultural advice.

This process provides a very simple means of degrading proteins that is cheap, efficacious, and simple to manage at any level in almost any circumstance—from a village home to an industrial facility—in almost any part of the world. It can be manipulated for the production of very specific crop-targeted individual products, with varied macro and micronutrient values, in order to design specific franchised and IP-protected output products.

One could argue that the process will only generate a value akin to the nutrient value of the input material. This is ostensibly inarguable; however, as demonstrated by previous research, recognition of the added biostimulant effects of these products is relatively new. The exciting aspect of this process is that the use of materials determined to be organic wastes—including road kill, post-production food waste, farm wastes, over-production crop wastes, feral animal culling, and domestic and industrial food wastes—all become potential inputs for food production.

These materials cycle back into the input role in a form that is readily accessible by living crops. Of additional benefit and interest to regulators is that the process itself denatures the proteins in the input product. Since the denaturing processes or reactions within it are not strong enough to break the peptide bonds, the primary structure, which is the basic sequence of amino acids, remains the same after denaturing.

Product Value and the Recycling Paradigm

The commercial value of the foliar spray developed using this method, in terms of waste organic products, has not as yet been fully appreciated. As a financial example, though, we can compare it to similar biostimulant products already on the market.

A biostimulant product from feral pig carcasses developed in recent research overseen by Dr. Sara Beavis of the Fenner School of Environment and Society at ANU, Canberra, Australia, was used in a comparative growth trial with a number of well-known foliar biostimulant brands by the Plant Accelerator in Adelaide, South Australia. The pig foliar biostimulant outperformed the majority of products in the trial, with the exception of those that had additional nutrient input.

Most of the products in the test cost wholesale for over $6 per quart. This means that a sale price of $3 per quart would be readily achievable for a beneficial biostimulant product made from any number of singular or mixed-waste materials. Such a product could be sold directly to farmers in bulk at approximately $3,000 per ton. This could be achieved without the additional costs of bottling for small-scale sales.

Within the recycling industry, the most valued recyclable material in terms of consistency of sale price is aluminum, which readily retains a market value of $1,500 per ton. Without the addition of any additional micro or macronutrients, biostimulant foliar fertilizers made from any domestic or commercial food waste would readily obtain a higher value than recycled aluminum. With adjusted macro and micronutrient levels, the sale price could be three or four times the value of the base hydrolysate.

As previously mentioned, a higher value could be obtained if specific products were made to suit a specific franchise or a designated crop. A testing regime could readily be established to provide a base level for product marketability. This process would make biostimulants, produced from a range of organic waste, the most valuable product in the recycled resources market. It also provides the opportunity, if more valuable products were made, to directly purchase source-separated, clean products from a range of sources.

This single function—the addition of commercial value to quality source-separated organic materials—would create an economic revolution in the recycling industry.

Biochar and the Down-Draft Gasifier

Biochar is a relatively new term among the more common understandings of charcoal products. It is a form of manufactured charcoal that can be made from a range of biomass sources.

The use of biochar as an agricultural input has a range of beneficial effects, from providing a living environment for microbes and increasing moisture retention to improving plant resilience and decreasing naturally occurring stresses. Asian rice farmers have used biochar as an additive for composting rice straw or, more directly, to increase crop yield.

Biochar is a fine-grained charcoal produced from high-temperature pyrolysis: the controlled burning of organic matter in a restricted oxygen environment. What differentiates biochar from charcoal is its purpose; if it is produced as an additive to soils, its main function will be to improve nutrient retention and carbon storage.

Charcoal in soils is an integral element of soil structure and, historically, its creation through bushfire and wildfire and its deposition in soils have meant that nature has always used it as a regenerative tool for soil carbon and moisture retention.

Research conducted by Australia's CSIRO found that in some estuarine systems charcoal can constitute a very high percentage of the organic material present in the soils under lakes and rivers.[39]

Relatively small amounts of biochar can create effects on crop yield and carbon sequestration, and interest has progressively risen, to the point where quality biochar is now quoted at around $2,500 per ton. Clearly this value will rise or fall depending on local use and opportunistic value. If environmentally safe processes can be developed that create no pollution and produce high quality product, the demand for biochar will grow.

The combination of the products and processes listed above highlight changes in the potential reuse or remanufacture of organic materials that have the potential to change our entire agricultural base. Used on combination with innovations in cover crop usage on farms, they provide humanity with the ability to solve many issues in relation to the waste of organic resources, to increase production, and to reduce input costs on farms around the world.

These processes put humanity on a road to Zero Waste, a path in which organic materials play the leadership role. Organic materials can have a value above and beyond that of any of the recycled products currently on the market.

---

39. Saran Sohi, et al., "Biochar, Climate Change and Soil: A Review to Guide Future Research," CSIRO Land and Water Science Report, February 2009.

Feral

To Ludwig Leichhardt lost to all
A feral father for the few
Who left an empty horse behind
To join with animals of kind

Explorers seeking theirs to find
A sunburnt land already found
A million years before their time
Unholy men on hallowed ground

They sought the mysteries of the past
But all but few forgot to ask
Where sustenance it could be found
For hollow men on hallowed ground

So, Leichhardt now cannot be found
And like so many of his kind
He slept on river pebbles round
And left his empty horse behind

CHAPTER 10
Life from Death

The concept of waste, apart from being a distortion of language, provides social permission to discard materials of any size and form that no longer provide a direct benefit to humanity. The greater percentage of discarded materials, without careful reuse or recycling, will inevitably contribute to some form of environmental contamination.

Most pollution is caused by the uncontrolled release of the outputs of industrial processes. In the main, these pollutants are molecular: heavy metals produced by burning coal and other fuels, the herbicides and pesticides in our soils and rivers, the outputs of materials incineration, and the acids in our air, water, and soils. This of course does not even touch upon the plastics in our seas, the content in our landfills, or the litter on our roads. While having a return value or deposit scheme on bottles or cans will no doubt make some form of difference in the long term, such a scheme only addresses a tiny percentage of certain types of drink containers. Such programs risk the development of a panacea approach to production, luring the public into thinking that their waste issues have been resolved. And even if such schemes operated in every country that uses some variation of English law, they would only impact 10 percent of the world's population. If the issue is about pollution caused by plastic, then the focus must be far more strategic. It must focus on stopping the use of hydrocarbons in plastic manufacturing and it must ensure that all plastics are made from carbohydrates.

The expression "don't know, don't care" is sometimes used to describe the attitude of the public to the environment and to recycling in particular. But surely, it must be asked, if people don't know, how can we expect them to care? The government of Wales and other zero-waste communities in the Zero Waste Europe network are demonstrating that informed people will become involved, and that people do indeed care if they are told why they need to take action and if they understand how they can be involved. Given the barrage of trivial communication people deal with daily, is it any surprise that they have a poor knowledge of their immediate environment? Some societies have become so inured to the drama of new information that they can no longer differentiate the true from the false, the well from the ill, the real from the unreal, or the safe from the dangerous. Media operators, business owners, and politicians lie to us with virtual impunity, and even when they are known to be wrong or lying, they rush on to the next trivial event in such a way that we have neither the time nor the temerity to challenge them.

Amidst this haranguing and mistrust, we have become progressively disconnected from our environment and the things that make it a viable haven for all living things. Few children understand or are taught the importance of death in the creation of life, the cycles of new replacing old, or the loss of diversity for simplicity. Nor are they taught the importance of biodiversity to the sustenance of all species. It can be the cause of great sorrow to contemplate that you may be listening to the call of a bird that your children's children may never hear.

In the space of half a potential Western human lifetime, our species, through its greed and avarice, has eliminated 60 percent of the mammals, bird, fish, and reptiles in the world. The World Wildlife Fund says we have managed to record this loss through human actions in less than 50 years since 1970. This period coincides with the social development of a cavalier attitude toward the effects of our blanket use of chemical fertilizers, herbicides, and pesticides, which, according to the UN, have reduced the capacity of industrial agriculture to only around 60 more harvests. We are told to trust the application of chemical science to food production, even when we are aware of the peer-reviewed tragedies of DDT, thalidomide, and agent orange.

From the soil and the sea to the sky and beyond, we have abused the protections, potentials, and potency of every aspect of our multi-species biosphere. We have degraded and denigrated the very elements of the "commons," which all species, including ourselves, need to survive. In the midst of all the measurable angst we have produced, and of all the harm and catastrophe we have brought upon ourselves and our fellow earth-bound species, the loss of biodiversity is a truly irreversible consequence. And the consequences are grave.

It is fundamental to the survival of the human species that we begin to move with both regard and respect back into the cycle of life that sustains us and all other living things. The structure and relationships inherent in biodiversity are our only protection against what Professor Garett Hardin referred to as the "Tragedy of the Commons," in which we all take what we want rather than what we need, ultimately destroying the whole.

With that, I come back to the central theme of this book: living on the planet as a natural animal in a natural system within closed cycles of production, where every output becomes an input for another—truly living zero waste. Humanity living on this planet earth as if we intend to stay.

We are, after all, the canary of our own coal mine.

We must recognize and learn to abhor the claptrap and drivel of misapplied science, which says we need genetically modified foods to produce the tonnages we need to feed humanity, while both science and economics say that we already produce more than enough to feed the entire world population. When food waste is 40 percent of total production, it is clearly politics and the perceived need to generate profit from wars and weapons sales that keep food from people's mouths. Even if money were all human existence were about, as much profit could be generated by feeding and housing people as from destroying their lives, homes, and livings through weapons and wars.

We must highlight any false and untested science that tells us it is safe to poison the soil and its biological processes to produce food. Such evil must be seen as inhuman in its very structure. The very elemental forms of biological delivery of nutrients to and from the roots of plants are forgotten in the midst of chemical fertilizer marketing.

Modern Western humanity has made many poor decisions in regard to the protection of life and the production of food.

Our waste outputs and the management of that waste clearly demonstrates a means of change and a point of connection for households and communities—to bring us back to both a connection with the soil and to the protection of our environment. Most importantly, the means to deliver that change in most Western communities is a cost we already pay—we have both the means and the money.

The key to maintaining the value of the materials we no longer have an immediate need for is source separation.

The models we need already exist in our human world and all are circular in form and function.

Implementing such models will be your future work—based not on the management of waste but on the sustenance of life.

Herein are the tools, and there is the future—we have been waiting for you to arrive.

The End

And there she sat straight legged on sea side sand
Her feet in waves washed clean from years of toil
Exhausted tears roll down upon her cheek
To meet with water's edge in quite relief
All going home and adding salt to salt
She cried for wind which longed to grip her skin
She cried for rain no longer falling into tides
She cried for man's simplicity
A short-lived work of wonder
A failed attempt of kind
Of justice limp and lost
That could not listen to the heart of hearts,
Where to now this listless soul of sea?
No more the ears to hear the song of birds
To understand the language of the loved
To feel a waters chill, a warmth of sun,
She knows the end has come
The rising tide upon her legs
Responds unto the moon
The moon unto the stars
The stars unto eternity
And there sits she
The mother of it all
And cries and
Cannot stop
The tears

About the Author

Gerry Gillespie has been involved in the recovery of organic materials and their reuse in agricultural soils for the past thirty years, both in Australia and overseas.

Following a leadership role in the No Waste by 2010 strategy for the Australian Capital Territory government, Gerry was asked to be the founding manager of the Zero Waste Trust in New Zealand. This subsequently led to his involvement in media communications and public speaking, addressing audiences at forums and events on resource recovery in the UK, France, New Zealand, the United States, Japan, China, and Taiwan.

Gerry is a founding member of the Zero Waste International Alliance and the Zero Waste International Trust, both of which were established at Beaumaris, Wales, in October 2003. He has also held positions on numerous boards, including Healthy Soils Australia, Zero Waste Australia, Zero Waste NZ Trust, Revolve, New South Wales Organics Round Table, International Biochar Initiative, the Asian Network of Organics Recyclers, and Rural Australians for Refugees, at which he served as the national executive and the president of the Queanbeyan branch.

In 2003, Gerry developed the highly successful City to Soil community engagement strategy, a program that collects clean organic waste and returns it as high-quality compost, reconnecting the urban community with their farmers. This strategy is being utilized by the Stump Jump Foundation in India and has been translated into Hindi and Punjabi.

Gerry's use of simple "open-source" composting processes, with little mechanical input and the application of organic inoculant fertilizer products, has given many remote communities, both in Australia and around the world, a highly effective and efficient means of enriching soils and managing resources.

A key objective of Gerry's work is to train local communities in the use of readily accessible technology that enables the most cost-effective use of organic waste in local food production systems.

Gerry continues to work with international communities, with recent engagements in Scotland, France, Egypt, and China. Over the past twenty years he has become a passionate activist and advocate for social justice and equality.

CPSIA information can be obtained
at www.ICGtesting.com
Printed in the USA
FSHW010256311019